"Aren't you curious about making love?"

As he spoke, Trent's eyes were luminous with ardent persuasion.

"Not with you, Trent," Felicity retorted.

Trent's expression hardened. "Can I be wrong, then? Do I repulse you so much? Do you hide a frigid heart beneath that gentle exterior?"

She wanted to cry out, *No, you're wrong. I want to be in your arms again, to experience the passion of your kiss.* But she held back. He was only playing with her, and it would amuse him greatly to know her true feelings.

"Perhaps I am frigid," she lied. "At any rate I don't go for short affairs. Go back to Crystal. She's more your type than I am."

"I will." Trent's voice held anger. "She's a damn sight less aggravating than you are!"

GWEN WESTWOOD
is also the author of these
Harlequin Romances

Many of these titles are available at your local bookseller.

For a free catalogue listing all available Harlequin Romances
and Harlequin Presents, send your name and address to:

HARLEQUIN READER SERVICE,
1440 South Priest Drive, Tempe, AZ 85281
Canadian address: Stratford, Ontario N5A 6W2

Dangerous to Love

by

GWEN WESTWOOD

Harlequin Books

TORONTO • LONDON • LOS ANGELES • AMSTERDAM
SYDNEY • HAMBURG • PARIS • STOCKHOLM • ATHENS • TOKYO

Original hardcover edition published in 1981
by Mills & Boon Limited

ISBN 0-373-02477-0

Harlequin edition published May 1982

CHAPTER ONE

THE little old English car, chugging along at a sedate thirty miles an hour, looked incongruous among the sleek, huge Canadian vehicles on the busy Montreal highway. Felicity Tait, sitting high in the leather passenger seat, tried hard to quell her growing impatience. Really, Wyatt's passion for driving his unstable vintage vehicle at a time like this was too much, especially as, with his usual disregard for punctuality, he had arrived half an hour later than he had said he would to take her to the airport.

She had been ready, dressed in her smart new pale blue uniform, for fully an hour before he had called for her. She had had too much time to contemplate her own reflection, to rearrange her red-gold hair into a still neater knot, to apply a little blue eyeshadow that emphasised even more the deep blue of her eyes.

She looked at her watch, the elegant digital with the blue face which had been supplied by the travel firm with whom she had obtained her new situation. She had been working for the same kind of firm in Quebec but, feeling in need of a change, had applied to Vancouver for a position, and this was where she was heading now. At least she hoped she was.

'Can't you make her go any faster, Wyatt?' she demanded. 'We haven't much time. You were rather late calling for me, you know.'

Wyatt smiled his lazy smile, only one hand on the wheel.

'No way, honey, but not to worry. Muppet will get you there, and if she doesn't, what's the hustle?

5

We can have another night on the town and you can go tomorrow.'

'But that's where you're wrong,' Felicity protested. 'I've got to catch this plane, otherwise I won't be able to connect with my group in Vancouver.'

The little high-built car, fire-engine red with burnished brass lamps, seemed to be going slower rather than faster. Oh, why did I let him persuade me to come in this? she thought. Why didn't I come in the airport bus as I'd intended? But he had been so pressing and she had felt sorry for him because he said he was in love with her and she was leaving him to go out West, possibly for a long time. Wyatt's old car was his pride and joy, but she had experienced too many breakdowns with it not to have realised that it was too temperamental a vehicle in which to travel to an airport, when there was an important connection to make.

'I never did think you should accept this post anyway,' said Wyatt. 'It's too far from Quebec, nearly five hours' flying time, three thousand miles away from all your friends. You won't like it there.'

To Felicity, beginning to feel more and more frustrated, the car seemed to be proceeding now at about ten miles an hour. Other cars were sweeping down around them in all directions, some of them blowing their horns impatiently. There was a tight band around her head from tension and anxiety, and she forgot that she had been feeling sorry for Wyatt, for all her thoughts were centred on trying to catch that plane.

'For heaven's sake, Wyatt,' she protested, 'we've had all this over before. It isn't the time to start an argument now. It's a wonderfully interesting job and I'm determined to go. Please, please, try to make Muppet go a bit faster!'

She usually refused to call his car by this ridiculous

name, but at the moment she felt she would do anything to placate him in order to arrive at the airport on time.

'She's doing her best for such an old lady,' said Wyatt.

His fair hair hung in a lock over his brows and he looked anything but worried about his car's performance or lack of it. Felicity felt a wave of irritation at the way he spoke of his car as if it were a human being and she looked with some envy at the sleek roadsters sliding past them. Yes, it was time she left Quebec. Wyatt had become too demanding in the last few months, too possessive, but she did not love him. There was a weakness in his personality that brought out some kind of maternal instinct in a woman, and she sensed that in such a marriage she would always have to be the stronger of the two. That was not what she wanted in a man.

But what did she want? She did not know. She had never yet met anyone with whom she felt she could spend a lifetime. Ah, well, she was only twenty-three. Early days yet. And yet it worried her that weaker men always seemed drawn to her. Perhaps her job as a courier for a travel agency had made her have to appear strong, for she had had to deal with crises, make decisions on her own for the good of a group of people of very varied kind.

The normal noise of Muppet's engine, something like that of a high-powered sewing machine, was interrupted by an ominous clanking. The little car began to proceed forward in alarming jerks and odd rumbling noises came from its interior, like the distant warning of some small volcano.

'What now?' asked Felicity, and with that Muppet shuddered protestingly and ground to a complete stop.

In the ensuing silence, Felicity was aware of the great planes tearing through the heavens above her, deafening the skies on their way to and from Dorval Airport. Odd, she thought, how much noise they make when you're on the ground and yet when you're inside them they seem to glide through the air like silk. Those planes will be landing in a few moments, but we're still a good twenty kilometres away, and at this rate it means another half hour.

'Why have we stopped?' she asked.

'I think it must be the fuel pump. I've thought for some time that she needs a new one.'

'Then, for heaven's sake, why didn't you see to it?' Felicity demanded. 'If you knew there was something wrong, why bring me out in this . . . this heap?'

'No need to be rude about Muppet,' said Wyatt, sounding aggrieved. 'She functions remarkably well on the whole.'

'But I need her to function now!'

Wyatt did not seem at all concerned at her agitation. He was not even attempting to look at the engine but had lit a cigarette and did not seem in the least hurry to investigate the trouble. Felicity felt beside herself with rage and frustration.

'May I ask what you're proposing to do about getting me to the airport?'

Wyatt's blue eyes regarded her with an innocence that she found suspicious.

'Nothing. You can phone them tomorrow and say you don't want the job. You could easily get your old one back here. You're too valuable to lose and they know it.'

'Oh, don't be crazy! I believe you're glad this has happened!'

Wyatt flicked the ash from his cigarette and smiled lazily.

'Of course I am. I've told you often enough you're the most attractive girl I've ever met. Why should I have to lose you that easily?'

Felicity gasped.

'You hoped this would happen! You've done it on purpose. You knew the car would break down and now you aren't doing anything about it. Well, if you won't, I will!'

With that she jumped out of the passenger seat and launched herself out into the middle of the busy highway.

'Come back, Felicity, don't be a fool!' she heard Wyatt shout, and then traffic was all around her, swerving, blowing long blasts on their horns. There was a small island in the middle of the highway and she reached this like a sailor escaping a horde of sharks, then stood on it frantically waving at passing traffic trying to flag some vehicle down.

From the tangle of traffic she saw a blue Cadillac, as big as a hearse, bearing down towards her island refuge and, bending forward, she waved to try to attract the attention of the uniformed driver, but as she did so, she overbalanced and fell right in the path of the speeding car. There was a wild squealing of brakes and she found herself sprawled upon the gritty road within inches of the now stationary vehicle, her pale blue uniform, of which she had been so proud, stained with fuel oil from the dusty road, her smart forage cap over one eye and the neat red-gold coiffure ruined, for her hair had descended to her shoulders.

Overhead she saw a silver plane swooping across the sky and remembered that she must, she simply *must* get to the airport on time, and then the blue sky behind the plane seemed to quiver and go black and she felt a sickening wave of giddiness as she tried to rise.

'Take it easy, and for the Lord's sake try not to faint,' she heard a voice say. 'I don't aim to cope with fainting females.'

The sky was blue again now but, instead of the plane in mid-air, there was a face. Masculine—

oh, yes, very masculine. But not Wyatt. Gold-green eyes under thick dark brows. Wavy dark hair springing strongly from a slight peak on the broad forehead. Face as brown as the hands that were touching her now, touching her with gentleness but a kind of hidden strength.

'Do you think you could stand now? Nothing seems to be broken. We'll try to get you into the car. I think I must take you to hospital for a check-up.'

'No—no hospital,' she managed to gasp. 'Got to make my plane. Must be in Vancouver tonight.'

'So how come you were perched up on that barrier in the centre of a busy highway? Damned odd way of catching a plane, if you don't mind my saying so. Never mind, spare me the explanations. You look all in. Let me get you to the car, we can talk later.'

'Wyatt?' she asked vaguely, and heard a murmur of voices, but then she felt herself lifted up and a wave of darkness descended upon her again. Semiconscious, she was glad to sink back against the great car's silver-grey cushions, deeply comfortable, conducive to a state of pleasant, suspended animation in which she was willing to nestle down and let the events of the last half hour fade into the background. She didn't know where Wyatt might be, and at the moment she did not really care. And she did not know who this tall, strong-armed stranger was or where he was taking her, but at the moment it did not seem to matter. She was aware that he was supporting her with his arm and that her face was against the soft lovat tweed of his shoulder, her tousled, silky red-gold hair beneath the square clear-cut lines of his chin.

'Well, this is all very pleasant, but I think we'd better find out about that plane. Are you sure you feel capable of travelling now?'

Felicity roused herself and sat up, trying to brush the hair from her eyes and make some attempt to revert to her usually calm, sure self. The automobile had stopped in front of the airport building and she heard her companion giving instructions to his driver.

'Thomas will find out about your plane and meanwhile we'll go in to the private lounge. I think we can make you more comfortable there.'

So he had access to the V.I.P. reception room. Felicity wondered fleetingly how this could be, but in her present dazed state was content to take everything for granted that was happening to her. They had only just entered the small room with its comfortable chairs and green potted plants when Thomas came back and whispered something to his employer. The words she heard with sinking heart were, 'No way.'

'Tough break, you've missed your plane. I rather thought this might happen. Even before you flung yourself under my car, you must have known there was very little chance of making it. Your boy-friend's automobile was interesting, but hardly the kind of vehicle to make up lost time. Why didn't you take the airport bus?'

'I wish I had,' said Felicity. 'Oh, what happened to Wyatt?'

'Wyatt's the boy-friend? He was very distressed about you, I can tell you that, but when I told him I'd get you to the airport, he unloaded your suitcase but decided it was best to stay with his car. He didn't want to risk having it towed away.'

No, thought Felicity bitterly. If it came to a choice between me and Muppet, I know who would win. At the moment she felt as if she didn't care if she never saw him again.

'What am I to do now?' she said aloud, but really talking to herself. 'I've wanted this job for ages, but if I let them down on my very first trip, they'll hardly keep me on.'

'Tell me about that later,' he said.

Of course he couldn't be interested. This must all seem very boring to him.

'Are you feeling a little sturdier now? How about going to wash some of the dust and grime off yourself and I'll order coffee, unless you'd like something stronger.'

'No, no, coffee would be fine.'

In the washroom, still feeling a bit shaky, she washed away the dust and did her best to clean off the blue uniform. As she brushed her red-gold hair down upon her shoulders, she decided to leave it long, because it seemed too much trouble to arrange it in the neat French pleat she usually wore beneath her cap. In the mirror, her dark blue eyes looked huge and startled. What an idiot this man must have thought her! She did not even know his name, and yet she had spent the last half hour lying relaxed in his arms as if he had been someone with whom she shared a most intimate friendship.

'Ah, that looks better. How about introducing ourselves? I'm Trent Seymour and you are . . .?'

'Felicity Tait. Look, Mr Seymour, I'm terribly sorry to have caused you so much trouble. I'll take myself off as soon as I've had this coffee. I must phone the travel company to tell them I can't make it. They'll have to get someone else to take this party through the Rockies.'

'We can drop the formalities. Our meeting was pretty informal anyway. Let's make it Trent, shall we? And may it be Felicity?'

'Yes, yes, I suppose so.'

She looked at him now, for the first time really taking in his appearance. He was a tall man with broad shoulders, but his hips were narrow and lithe as an athlete's. Gold-green eyes beneath dark, straight brows looked directly into her own. It would be difficult to tell a lie to this man, she thought.

Trent Seymour? Hadn't she read somewhere a profile about a man of that name who had all kinds of interests in the way of mining, but who owned cattle ranches too, a man who had pushed himself up from being a prospector in the Yukon and the wild places of the North and was now a millionaire with a finger in many concerns? Was this he? It seemed more than likely.

It hardly mattered, she thought, whether he called her by her first name or not. After today she would never see him again. Her life did not lie in the same direction as a millionaire's and the casual kindness he had shown her meant nothing.

'I must go and find a phone,' she said.

'Not so fast. I have another suggestion. I'm taking off to Vancouver myself as soon as I can get my plane cleared.'

'Your plane?' she queried.

'For my own convenience, I have the kind of plane they call an executive jet. It's just a small one, takes about eight people, but as it happens I'm travelling alone to Vancouver today. I can easily take you with me if you promise to let me get on with some work and not do too much chattering.'

His brusque manner somehow belied the kindness of his offer.

'I have to do enough talking in my work to appreciate being quiet on occasions, and I suppose I could sit at the back of the plane,' she said.

He looked amused and it occurred to her that this was the first time she had seen him smile. It was a smile of some considerable charm. No wonder he had succeeded in business! She regretted having spoken so sharply.

'I'm sorry. It's more than kind of you to offer me a flight, Mr . . . I mean Trent. It would be marvellous if I could get there on time. It would make all the difference to me, to my whole life, in fact.'

'That sounds very dramatic. What about your young man? There's a phone over there. Do you want to let him know what's happening?'

'He'll hardly be home yet—and he's not my young man, although he did his best to keep me here. I'll let him know later.'

Felicity still could not help feeling bitter about Wyatt and his failure to get her to the plane. It had seemed almost deliberate. Let him worry about her for a while longer—that was, if he should be worrying, which she doubted.

In what seemed no time at all she was seated in the neat, elegant small jet plane, and when she moved to sit at the back, as she had vowed she would, he motioned her to come and sit beside him.

'I thought you wanted to work,' she said.

'There'll be plenty of time for that after we've had some kind of meal. Let's see what the store cupboard has to offer, shall we? Do you like champagne?'

'I would prefer that fresh orange juice.'

'Good girl, so would I. How about smoked salmon with brown bread and butter and perhaps a few spears of asparagus?'

'Gorgeous,' said Felicity, thinking that by now she would have been eating the usual plastic food served on a large jet if she had caught her plane.

Meanwhile the pilot had taxied the plane to its taking off point at the end of the runway where he had to wait his turn for permission to take off. Soon they were in the air, high above Montreal. The square sections of streets swung below them and already the city lights were pricking out diamond patterns, and then they were above the clouds heading over the vast stretch of land that was Canada.

'We're three hours behind Vancouver time, as you know. We'll probably land there with any luck at about nine their time. Are you feeling fit enough to start out on this trip of yours tomorrow?'

'I must be fit enough whatever happens,' said Felicity. 'It's a pearl of a job. I've wanted to do it for ages.'

If she had told him the truth, she would have had to admit that she still felt a bit weak and shaken by the events of the afternoon, but it was nothing, she believed, that a good night's rest wouldn't cure.

'What exactly is this position you're heading for?'

'I'm going to be courier to a coachload of people touring the Rockies. It's such wonderful scenery. I'm almost as excited about it as they must be.'

'Do you know the Rockies?'

'I don't know everything about this particular trip, but I've been coached theoretically over the whole route and the driver is experienced. He's a very good driver and he'll be able to help me out over the places where I'm ignorant.'

'Interesting. I didn't know they sent women as couriers on these rugged tours.'

'Why not? It's not all that rugged. We stay in motels and I can cope with people on tour better than most men can, I assure you.'

'I don't doubt it. One look at those large blue eyes and that chestnut red hair could quell most complaints, I would say.'

She looked at him cautiously. His expression was somehow different, as if he had just discovered what she looked like. Take care, Felicity, she told herself. This man has oodles of charm and knows how to use it.

'I hope there needn't be any complaints on this particular tour,' she said. 'In fact it all sounds absolutely heavenly and I hope it will be.'

'You make it sound like Paradise, but all the same I don't envy you having to shepherd a probably ill-assorted group, even if it is through all that natural magnificence. And in a coach too. I can't remember when I travelled in a coach last.'

'You should try it some time. It would be a novelty to you.'

'You almost tempt me to try. In my varied career there was a time when I had to earn my keep by driving a coach, so you see I'm not without some experience. How about trying to get me a job with your company?'

'You must be joking!'

'Well, perhaps I am, but at the moment I think it might be quite a good idea to take a job as a driver. It would be wonderful to get away somewhere for a couple of weeks and not even have the telephone to contend with, much less my brokers and accountants.'

He put his hand to his head, where Felicity noticed there were some small furrows in the dark brow.

'Yes, I could do with some relaxation,' he went on. 'Actually that's why I'm going to Vancouver. I have a house there perched above the water on the west side. I'm hoping to be undisturbed for a few days, do a spot of fishing and sailing. But I guess it's a bit hopeless if I stay in Vancouver. There's always someone after me there.'

Sitting beside him, Felicity was a little too aware of him, the warmth of his thighs in the lovat tweed suit, the brown hands gesticulating as he spoke. Rather long fingers. Not, she would have thought the hands of a self-made man who spent a lot of his youth, it was said, panning for gold in out-of-the-way places.

'Don't you have any other place to go to?' she asked.

'I'll probably go to my ranch up West when I've tired of sailing, but even there the phone makes one very vulnerable, and there are other reasons too why it isn't so restful there.'

A woman? she hazarded a guess.

'Are you married?' she asked him before she had time to consider whether that might be an impertinent question from such a recent acquaintance. But he took her hand in his large brown one and contemplated its small slender fingers devoid of any rings.

'Hardly,' he said. 'I tend not to go for long attachments. There's one woman I've loved all my life, but that's a different story. Marriage is for other men. It may be good for some people, but not for me. However, I take my pleasures where I find them. And you? Or is that indiscreet to ask?'

'No. I'm going to Vancouver to start a new life, I hope. At this moment I'm rather tired of men.'

'Or of one man in particular? Don't worry, my dear. If you want him back, he'll probably come running.'

'You make him sound like some kind of puppy dog! Anyhow, I don't want him to come running. I prefer to put my past life behind me now. And marriage is not included in my plans either.'

'You sound very fierce about it. Must be that red hair that makes you so, though I must admit it looks very beautiful, like silky gold-red fire, the kind of gold a man sets his heart on when he's young and foolish and full of strange desires.' As if stirred by a sudden impulse, he leaned towards her and touched her hair. 'Yes, just as I thought. It feels as good as it looks. If women knew how it stirs a man they'd all wear their hair long.'

'But what if they don't want to stir them?'

As she felt the soft touch of his hand on her hair, she had been alarmed at the sudden unbidden, sensual thrill that seemed to originate from somewhere deep inside her body.

'Ah, Felicity, don't try to play the Puritan with me. I'm too old a hand at the game of love. Your appearance couldn't possibly conceal a frigid nature. No, my dear, it's plain to me those lips were created for kissing.'

His hand was on her shoulder now and the other one reached out until it was under her chin, turning her face towards him until her mouth, that mouth he had praised, was only inches from his own.

'Why are you trembling?' he queried. 'Do you think I'm the kind of man who would take advantage of this promising situation? Well, let me tell you, my dear Felicity, you're right, and I am.'

'I have no doubt of that,' she said, trying to smile and pass off this rather alarming conversation in a casual manner. 'You may think the situation is promising, but I don't. I'm myself not just a situation and I don't promise anything to strange men, however kind they happen to have been to me.'

Really it was stupid to feel like this. In her travel job, she had met all manner of people and learned how to deal with all kinds of men, and their various approaches. It must be the accident that was making her feel so shaky.

'Isn't it time I went to the back of the plane?' she asked. 'I think I badly need to rest. That fall shook me up more than I realised at the time.'

Trent Seymour smiled and she smiled back at him, relieved that his hand had let go of her chin and she could now turn around and be free of his devastating nearness.

'Ah, well, Felicity, we'll let you off this time. At least you aren't pleading the usual feminine excuse, a headache.'

As she tried to rise from the low comfortable seat, she felt her legs almost give way beneath her, and she stumbled and would have fallen except that Trent quickly got up and put his arm around her, supporting her in the aisle of the plane.

'What's all this, then? You really do need some

rest, don't you? Let's get you in to the back seat with your feet up and I'll get a blanket and tuck you in.'

Again she was glad of his strong support as she found her way through the cabin to the rear of the plane where he insisted on taking her shoes off. She felt his hands on the front of her tight jacket undoing the fastenings.

'Don't be alarmed,' he told her. 'Merely a practical measure for your comfort. I know that much at least about fainting females, clothing should be loose.' He swung her in to a reclining position on the wide seat and tucked a warm blanket around her. 'There, that's better, and when you've had a couple of hours' sleep, you'll feel like a new woman, I hope.'

Felicity lay there feeling utterly relaxed now, lapped in warm comfort. Beyond the porthole, she could see a landscape of clouds like snowy mountains and every now and again there was a break of deep cobalt blue with silvery stars sweeping across the heavens. The scene with Trent had had a strange effect on her. She did not feel annoyed at his approach. Rather when she thought of his mobile mouth that had been so close to her own, close enough for kissing, as he had perhaps intended it to be, she felt again the thrilling sensation that had in it half fear, half fascination. Ridiculous, she told herself. You've met plenty of other men, Felicity, and you've learned often enough, in a rugged way, to keep out of harm's way. Harm? I guess a man of his kind thinks it almost obligatory to make a pass at an attractive girl if he senses the opportunity. It didn't mean a thing. He just happens to have the kind of looks that stops a girl in her tracks, and I should think he knows it too.

The stars spun around through the porthole and her lids drooped. Some time later Trent came quietly up the gangway, walking remarkably softly

for a man of his size, but he need not have bothered.
Felicity was sound asleep, looking like a red-haired
angel, very young and vulnerable, very far removed
from the impression of efficient young travel courier
that she strove so hard to create in her working hours.

CHAPTER TWO

THE last remnants of the sunset showed in wisps of
rosy cloud as they flew in to Vancouver, but below
them the circle of gleaming starry lights made it look
like some magical city of dreams. Felicity felt almost
reluctant to wake up to reality as the plane landed
smoothly and she felt the ground beneath them.

'It looked so gorgeous from the air,' she said to
Trent.

'Beautiful from the ground too,' he agreed. 'One of
the most beautiful cities in the world. Now tell me,
where were you intending to stay before all this
happened?'

She gave him the name of the hotel, one of those
vast multi-roomed buildings on the harbourside,
especially created to deal with hundreds of tourists
passing through.

'Nonsense, you can't stay there tonight—it's as
impersonal as a public washroom. I must know
whether your mishap caused you any lasting harm.
I propose to take you to my house and call a doctor.'

'But really, Mr Seymour ... Trent, there's
absolutely no need. I feel great now, and when I've
had a good night's sleep. . . .'

'In that rabbit warren? No, Felicity, I propose
that you have a good night's sleep in more pleasant
surroundings.'

'It's most kind of you, but I couldn't. I . . . I'd much prefer to be on my own.'

'You mean without me? Good grief, girl, what's wrong? Are you afraid of me? You can't imagine I intend to seduce you on so short an acquaintance?'

Looking at his brilliant eyes, the vigorous growth of his dark hair, the whole vital aspect of the man, Felicity thought that was just what she had been thinking.

'If I must,' she said, 'I'll come with you to see a doctor at his rooms, but afterwards I insist that you send me back to the hotel. I'm used to managing on my own and tomorrow I have to take charge of a whole crowd of people. I'm not exactly a helpless female, you know.'

'I don't think for a moment that you are. In fact you're acting far too damned independent right this minute. However, if you've at least consented to see my doctor, that's progress. As to what happens later, we shall see.'

Another driver, another beautiful car awaited him. How on earth many did he have? thought Felicity.

'Hi, Randy, how's tricks? All set for that poker game tonight?'

The driver was a thickset man who looked as if he could have been chosen for some heavyweight ability to throw out unwanted guests. Maybe poker was a good pastime for him, Felicity reflected as she sank into the spacious back seat and Trent, ignoring her, sat next to the driver. Certainly this Randy had shown no surprise at her presence with Trent. Did that show that he was used to Trent arriving for his vacation with a woman? Felicity thought darkly that it did. But what had it got to do with her anyway however many women Trent chose to bring from Montreal? She had consented to be examined by a doctor, although by now she felt perfectly well, but after that they would go their separate ways and she need never see this rather arrogant, disturbing stranger again.

Felicity had thought she had made it clear to Trent Seymour that she consented to see his doctor at his consulting rooms, but soon it was evident that Trent had other ideas.

'When we arrive down town you can drive us through Chinatown and Gas Town,' she heard Trent say to Randy. 'Our passenger has never been in Vancouver before, so she may as well see the sights.'

'I thought we were going to the doctor's rooms,' Felicity objected.

'All in good time. You may as well see the city. It looks pretty good at night, don't you think?'

They were now in an area of quaint shops where crowds of people lined the sidewalks. Lamps, imitating old gas standards, decorated the streets and the shops were full of tempting goodies. Felicity caught glimpses of Indian wood carvings, shoes and bags of soft, light brown suede, Eskimo whales, polar bears and seals in soapstone, and into the car drifted the most enticing smells—spices, curries, Oriental fragrances mingling with the more homely smell of baking bread and the piquant odours of Italian food, so that Felicity found her mouth watering and wondered when and where she would be able to eat this evening. Probably hamburger and French fries, she thought, ordered from room service, yet even the thought of such an ordinary meal was enough to make her feel hungry.

Soon they were out of Gas Town and making their way west along busy streets between great cliffs of buildings, shops, business places and the occasional hotel. There were a couple of older buildings with green, quaintly shaped copper roofs, similar to the older buildings she had known in Montreal, but for the most part the functional black glass expanses reaching into the sky looked like some city of the future.

And now there was a gentler scene, with spacious houses surrounded by the foliage of beautiful trees and there were glimpses of the harbour with busy ferryboats like toys on the large expanse of water. All this time Felicity had been enthralled by the new scene, and it was only when the Cadillac turned north over a long suspension bridge across the inner harbour that she began to wonder how far Trent was taking her to this doctor of his.

'Your doctor must live a long way from town,' she said.

Trent laughed.

'He's a good guy, a friend of mine. When I explain the set-up he'll come to the house. Don't worry about it. If he thinks you need an X-ray or whatever, he'll have you in hospital soon enough.'

Felicity sighed. How had she got into this situation? Here she was being driven far away from the hotel where she should be at this moment in a strange town with a man who had himself implied that he never missed an opportunity to make love to a pretty girl.

'I feel perfectly well now,' she assured him. 'I suppose you want the doctor to give me a clean bill of health because of some wretched insurance, but I assure you I'm not the kind of person who would sue anyone for damages when there isn't a thing wrong with me.'

'Just a precaution, a sensible one. I'm sure you would agree if you'd had as much to do with mercenary females as I have.'

'I'm not mercenary,' Felicity assured him. 'But I guess you and I live in different worlds. It wouldn't occur to me to try to sue you when I'm quite aware that the whole incident was entirely my own fault.'

'Do you hear that, Randy? Remember it. I may need to use you as a witness.'

'Oh, good grief!' exclaimed Felicity, now thoroughly exasperated. 'It must be weird to think of everything that happens in terms of money, and what people may get out of you. I don't know how you can stand it.'

'You'd be surprised, honey. If you'd had as hard a struggle for it in the first place as I had, money could mean an awful lot. I believe it means as much to me as a wife or children to other men.'

'Well, never having had much, I wouldn't know. I've managed to see quite a lot of the country in my work without needing much money, and I keep happy too.'

'Good for you!'

His smile was not a smile. In fact it was almost a sneer. Felicity felt he was mocking her. I suppose to a man like that what I said sounded very Pollyanna-ish philosophy, she thought. Well, why should I care? It sounds horrible to say that money can take the place of a wife or children, doesn't it?

They were driving now on a road that was high above the waters of the bay and behind them the main city of Vancouver on the farther shores glittered with lights.

'There's my house,' said Trent.

Felicity leaned forward and peered out into the dark. They were above a curving bay and on the cliff face a white house seemed to hang in space. It was lit from all sides like a Son et Lumière production and it looked like some architect's weird dream of a child's house of blocks, clinging to the cliff by means of stilts.

'How do you like it?' asked Trent.

Felicity looked at the arrogant tilt of his head and for a moment felt very tempted to say, 'It's horrible,' just to take him down for five seconds, but thought better of it.

'It's amazing,' she told him. 'How do you get down to it?'

'By an elevator, how else?' He dismissed the driver, saying, 'See you later, Randy. Mustn't miss my poker game. This time I'm going to beat the lot of you!'

Randy's response was a grunt as he drove off towards a block of buildings on the cliff top that presumably housed cars and staff. And then they were alone. A wind was blowing from the harbour mouth, smelling of sea and timber and bringing back folk memories of times before steam replaced sail. Up to now Felicity had been with Trent in thoroughly modern surroundings, an airplane, an automobile, a city new as tomorrow, but now the night was all around them and the city seemed far away. She shivered.

'Are you cold? We'll soon have you into the warmth.'

She felt his arm go around her shoulders as he drew her towards what seemed to be the cliff face itself. He spoke into the night and a strange disembodied voice replied.

'Like getting into Fort Knox,' commented Felicity.

'Not quite,' Trent replied, 'but these days you can't be too careful.'

A part of what had seemed to be the cliff swung silently aside and Trent ushered her into a small elevator that was lined with embossed blue velvet. His arm still remained around her and she was painfully conscious of it, but in this small space felt unable to shrug it aside. She was glad when in a few moments the door slid open and they stepped out into light and warmth.

Felicity smiled.

'I feel as if I really have come to Fort Knox,' she

said, for the large room glowed with gold—pale gold carpet with Persian rugs of blue and gold on its vast expanse, cream leather sofas, deep and inviting, with gold and blue velvet cushions, gilded lamps sending pools of light to show eccentric carvings in a gold-coloured wood.

'It's a beautiful room,' she commented.

'Yes, I think it's quite successful. The decorators did a good job on it.'

'You left it to other people?'

'Sure. Always call in the experts. They know about furniture, I know about mines. Makes sense, doesn't it?'

'It seems rather impersonal. Would you go to a marriage broker for a wife, then?'

'Hey, hold on! Who's talking about wives? I wouldn't go anywhere for one, so quit that kind of talk. I told you wives don't figure in my scheme of things. Women maybe, they have their uses, but definitely not wives. I've escaped them so far and I don't aim to start. If I do I'll be paying alimony to half a dozen before I know where I'm at.'

'Why anticipate that? Some marriages last, you know.'

'Show me some. No, girl, I've always believed in that maxim about he travels fastest who travels alone, and I'll stick by that.'

'In my kind of work, travelling fast isn't considered necessary,' said Felicity. 'You possibly get more out of life if you travel a bit more slowly.'

'That's not my way,' Trent assured her. 'It wouldn't suit me. All the same right at this moment I wouldn't mind a trip through the Rockies at your pace and not a telephone in sight.'

'Why don't you do it some time, then?'

'My business associates would catch up on me even there. No, to do it successfully I'd have to have some kind of disguise.'

'Well, I guess it must be great to feel so wanted,' said Felicity drily. The man's conceit is enormous, she thought, but I guess all selfmade men are like that.

He glanced at her sharply, sensing the sarcasm in her voice, but he did not reply and his silence somehow made her feel cheap. After all, if it hadn't been for him she would have had to resign her new post. He had been kind to her in his way. How could he help the fact that his whole personality, aggressive, demanding, self-satisfied, jarred on her?

'I'll show you to one of the guestrooms,' he told her. 'You might like a shower before the doctor arrives. I'll phone him while you're doing that.'

Another elevator and an illuminated passage doors leading off. Trent opened the door of a room that glowed as vividly pink as the living room had been gold. It was beautiful in a flamboyant way—pink satin bedhead on the huge bed with its vividly flowered coverlet, deep white carpet that one's feet sank into, crystal chandeliers and Tiffany lamps that cast a discreet glow over the scene, and a large painting of a woman on the wall, more than lifesize, with what seemed to Felicity to be acres of naked rosy flesh.

'I see your suitcase is here, but don't bother to unpack,' Trent advised her. 'You'll find everything you need in the way of cosmetics in the bathroom and there are plenty of bathrobes in that cupboard. When my doctor arrives, he can examine you here. Much more comfortable than his rooms would be, you must admit.'

Felicity found herself alone before she could reply. She looked all around her. There were exquisite silver brushes and combs on the large dressing chest, and when she opened the closet there were several robes in soft satin encrusted with lace. She looked in questioning fashion at the woman on the wall and that lady seemed to gaze quizzically back at her.

'If only you could speak,' Felicity said to her. 'Anyhow, you don't seem to feel the need for satin bathrobes sitting there on your pink clouds.'

In the bathroom she found a French cologne that she had always wanted to try but never been able to afford, and she made full use of it, together with the matching bath essence.

'I'll give the doctor a treat,' she told the naked lady on her pink cloud, and in the rosy glow of the shaded lamps the woman in the picture seemed to be giving her a naughty knowing smile.

'Isn't there another man you want to impress?' she seemed to be asking.

'Certainly not!' Felicity told her, and was then thoroughly startled by a soft knock on her door. Discreetly the good-looking doctor had brought a nursing Sister with him and together they examined Felicity very thoroughly. As she herself had thought, they could find nothing wrong with her except for some slight scratches and bruises.

'You're a very fortunate young lady,' the doctor assured her. 'It could have been much more serious. I'll leave a tablet to calm you down a bit, something to soothe your nerves, and after a good night's sleep you'll be as good as new. Goodnight, my dear. Sleep well.'

'Thank you very much for both coming so promptly,' Felicity said.

'You're welcome. Don't go falling under any more automobiles in the future. Next time you might not be so lucky.'

'And I can start work tomorrow?' asked Felicity.

'Certainly. It should be a kind of vacation for you. Get away to the Rockies and you can forget the whole thing. I wish I were coming with you.'

So now I can go, thought Felicity, when she was

left alone. I'll ask Trent to call a cab and in half an hour or less I should be at my hotel. What if it is as impersonal as a public washroom as Trent told me? This kind of room isn't my scene anyway. When I get there I'll put on my towelling bathrobe and I'll call room service and I'll have a double helping of hamburger and French fries and a mug of strong coffee. I don't care if it does keep me awake. And I'll not think any more about this rosy pink room and the rosy pink woman on the wall and who it is who owns all these silver brushes and the French perfume and the satin robes.

The pale pink house phone beside the bed trilled like a fairy flute.

'Hi.' It was Trent's voice. 'Dr Mackenzie says you're sound in wind and limb, but he feels you should rest, so my manservant is bringing a meal up to your room and I'll join you there, if that's all right with you.'

'Oh, there's no need,' Felicity said hastily. She knew that her voice was trembling and made a great effort to sound more firm. 'If you could call a cab, I can go to my hotel. It's very kind of you to offer me a meal, but I can easily get something from room service when I get there.'

'Nonsense! Weldon is on his way up to you right now. I hope you like entrecôte steak with mushrooms and French fries, because that's what you're getting. Can you drink red wine?'

'Yes, but. . . .'

'Great! See you.'

There was no time now to change back into her tailored suit. She was still in the pale peach satin robe with its deep appliqué of coffee-coloured lace around the low cut of the bodice. Her hands trembled as she tried to fasten the row of tiny buttons with their little satin loops. Should she tie back her

hair? It was descending in red-gold waves around her
shoulders. But no, the plain navy ribbons she used for
this purpose were in her overnight bag, and before she
had a chance to find them, there was a knock at the
door and a manservant entered with a laden trolley.

'Good evening, miss. My name's Weldon. Mr
Seymour says he'll be up in a minute.'

He was an older man than Trent's driver, with a
narrow face and the expression of a cynical monkey.
By his accent, Felicity did not think he could be
Canadian.

'Are you from England?' she asked him, as he
started to set a small table with places for two.

'I am, miss. I came to Mr Trent's service from being first footman to a duke, but I always fancied
Canada and so far it hasn't let me down!'

'I'm from England too. I've only been here a
couple of years.'

'What part, miss?'

'London.'

'Then we're both Cockneys, because I come from
there too.'

He inspected her more closely and she was conscious of her appearance as it must seem to him, the
clinging satin robe with the lacy plunging neckline
revealing more than it concealed, the shining hair
falling in disarray on her shoulders, and the alluring
French perfume filling the rosy room with its sensual
fragrance.

'This isn't me,' she wanted to say. 'I don't usually
look like this.'

He did not say any more and, after that one swift
glance, went on setting the table carefully and
neatly, but in that one look he had seemed to her to
say, 'And what's a nice girl like you doing in a
situation like this?' and she had felt even more ur-
gently the need to get away. Was he used to Trent

entertaining girl-friends in these surroundings? She wished she had insisted on getting dressed and dining in less compromising circumstances. That one glance from Weldon's old, world-weary eyes had told her what he was thinking of her. Well, but what did it matter anyway? She was not Trent's latest girl-friend, and soon she would be on her way back to the familiar surroundings of an ordinary tourist hotel.

Trent came in before Weldon had finished the arrangement of the table. He had changed out of his dark business suit and was wearing casual slacks and a striped cotton shirt.

'I hope that wine has been opened for at least an hour,' he said to Weldon.

Weldon seemed to draw himself up to his full height of five foot two and his monkey face looked more disapproving than it had been before.

'Certainly, sir. I know how to treat a good wine with the respect it deserves.'

'Good man, Weldon. Wine and women should always be treated that way. Don't you agree, Felicity?'

'I'm not sure. Who's to be the judge of what respect a woman deserves?'

'Why, her lover, of course, or the man who intends to be. But it takes an experienced man to judge a woman's character—or for that matter the character of a wine. And I'm an expert on both. Isn't it so, Weldon?'

'If you say so, sir.'

'Weldon's a mysogynist, aren't you, Weldon?' grinned Trent.

'Sir?'

'In plain words, you don't like women.'

'No, that's not true. I like respectable women, sir.'

It was almost as if he had added the words, 'But not the ones who come here.' His meaning was very plain to Felicity, but Trent did not seem to notice. His eyes were upon her and there was something in his expression that brought a warm rush of blood to her face.

'That robe is very becoming, my dear. You look somewhat different from the uniformed courier who first cast herself across my path. And thank you for leaving your hair loose. You look like a Botticelli angel—and yet I hope this particular one is not too angelic and that she has more appetite than an angel if she's going to do justice to Weldon's cooking. So, Weldon, how's the steak?'

The table was placed beside a deep window seat and Felicity found herself seated next to Trent as she had been on the plane. When Weldon had poured the wine and put a generous helping of steak on to their plates, Trent dismissed him.

'We won't need you again this evening. I'll put the trolley into the kitchen shaft when we've finished. Have you made the coffee? Ah, yes, I see it's there. Good, then that will be all, Weldon. I'll see you in the morning.'

'Doesn't he belong to your poker school?' asked Felicity as the door closed quietly behind Weldon.

'My . . .? Oh, no. He's rather a Puritan, is Weldon. Disapproves of wine, women and song and doesn't believe in gambling.'

'Good for him,' said Felicity.

'Don't tell me you're a Puritan too, because I just won't believe it. You're too beautiful to be disapproving of the good things in life.'

'That depends what you consider are the good things,' Felicity told him.

'Well, right now one of the good things in my life is this steak. Let's get on with it, shall we? And first you must taste this wine. I rather pride myself on being a good judge of wine and this is a particularly fine vintage. See how you like it.'

Felicity sipped her wine cautiously.

'Yes, it is delicious,' she said, putting the glass down.

'Why, you've hardly tasted it. Drink up, girl, we have a whole bottle to finish.'

'I'm afraid I won't be much help, then,' she told him. 'I'm not used to drinking wine.'

'All the more reason to enjoy it, then. Come along. It won't do you any harm.'

But Felicity was determined to keep her wits about her. She had begun to mistrust this whole set-up and wished she had insisted on going back to the hotel in the first place.

Trent was sitting beside her, the warmth of his body very close to her satin-clad thigh. It was not a disagreeable sensation—far from it. She moved away so that there was some distance between them and tried to concentrate on the meal, which was quite delectable. The steak seemed to melt in the mouth and the French fries were crisp and golden, unlike any she had ever tasted before. She stole a glance at Trent and surprised a smile which seemed secretive and not for her. Had he noticed the way in which she had drawn herself away from him? And what was there to amuse him in that? He should have got the message that she was not interested in him one little bit.

When they had finished eating he deftly piled the dishes on to the trolley, leaving the wine and glasses on the table.

'I won't be drinking any more,' Felicity informed him.

'You really are very abstemious. I must teach you to appreciate the good things in life a little more than that.'

'You won't have much time to teach me, will you? Really, Trent,' she added, 'I think I should be going. If you would call a cab for me I could be back at my hotel in half an hour. Now that you know I'm not hurt, there's no further reason for me to stay.'

'You amaze me,' he drawled. 'You prefer to spend
the night in that rabbit warren when you could spend
the night here in comfort? I'll see that you get back in
good time to make your arrangements for the tour.'

'No, really, Trent. You've been most kind, but I
would prefer to go now.'

'Let's discuss it over another glass of wine, shall
we? I'll take this trolley to the service escalator and
then we can talk at leisure.'

In his absence, Felicity paced across the room
restlessly. He seemed determined to keep her here
and she supposed it sounded sensible, considering
her accident, to stay here and go in the morning
instead of making the long journey back so late at
night. But I don't trust him, she thought. He's too
charming and too sure of his own attraction—which,
I must admit, is considerable. As she heard his returning steps, that were muffled by the velvet pile of
the carpet, she was surprised by a small frisson of fear,
but she did not know whether it was Trent or herself of whom she was afraid.

She was standing in front of the mirror now and
she was surprised by her own appearance, so
different from that of every day. The peach-coloured
satin clung smoothly over the curves of her breasts,
disclosing the small, round fullness as if indeed she
were as scantily dressed as the lady on the wall, and
it seemed to emphasise the curve of her hips before
falling to her feet in smooth folds. Her hair, a lighter
red-gold in the rosy light, framed her face in soft
waves and her face had a radiant glow, surely caused
by the surrounding colour of the room.

Through the mirror she saw the door open and the
shadowed figure of Trent, seeming larger than life,
was silhouetted for a moment against the light of the
corridor, then he was closing the door and it seemed
to her for a wild moment that he was about to lock it.

But instead he strode into the room to where she was standing. She felt his arms go around her waist and saw the reflection in the mirror of herself and the bronzed hands of the man behind her, holding her close against the hard muscles of his chest.

'Do you know how lovely, how very desirable you look right at this moment?' he murmured into her hair. 'Look at yourself. Aren't you the beautiful one?'

The reflection in the mirror seemed to Felicity to belong to another world. It was like looking at herself in a dream. Could this be she, the staid, sensible courier, whom other people had learned to rely upon, this wild, lovely creature with the revealing gown and the rosy parted lips?

With a muttered exclamation Trent had turned her around and, before she closed her eyes, she saw an extended view of herself in his arms, for there was another mirror on the opposite wall, and there they were, herself and this man, who until a few hours ago had been a stranger to her, little figures stretching into infinity, caught in each other's embrace.

His mouth descended upon hers, hard and demanding, and she felt herself pliable as candlewax in the strong circle of his arms. The gown slipped from her shoulders and she was aware of the roughness of his dark hair as his head went down and his mouth sought the curves beneath the softly sensuous silk. She was being borne along on a wave of emotion so intense that she knew she was experiencing something entirely new, and while her physical self begged to know the promised thrill of fulfilled desire, another part of her was desperately and darkly afraid.

'This is madness,' she protested. 'I hardly know you, Trent, and after tomorrow I'll never see you again.'

'What does that matter?' he demanded, his voice low and sounding hoarse. 'You can't deny this desire we feel for each other tonight, here and now. I'm in the habit of getting what I want, and tonight I want you. You must feel that. But why waste words when we can share this most beautiful sensation?'

He made to take her in his arms again, but his words had restored her to some kind of sanity.

'Oh, no, Trent! I told you before I'm not just a situation nor just an experience. I'm me, Felicity Tait, and I don't see myself as—what's the vulgar phrase?—a one-night stand. Just because you're in the habit of getting what you want, it doesn't mean you can have me.'

'Oh, come, Felicity, we're adult people, and you look too damned alluring in that garment to pretend that you're frigid. I promise you, you'll enjoy a night spent with me.'

He reached towards her, but she drew back.

'No, Trent, I'm not here to be made use of. You must have other girl-friends who are willing and able to make you happy, but this is definitely not my scene. I don't give myself to men I've only known for a few hours. Even you can't be sufficiently arrogant to think that of me.'

His hand came out and with those long fingers he traced the line of her cheek, then the curve of her neck and the satin-clad curve below. The caress was as gentle as the soft feathers of a dove and yet, in the mocking glint of those gold-green eyes, Felicity sensed the coiled strength of a leopard. His touch aroused some tremulous response deep in her body, but she determinedly ignored it.

'I'd like to be alone,' she said.

'Why are you trembling?' Trent asked softly. 'There's no need to be afraid. I've never taken any woman against her will.'

I'm afraid of myself, she thought.

'Please go,' she begged.

'If you wish it.'

'I do,' she said, but at the same moment she was shamed to feel a burning desire to be in his arms again.

'What a pity,' said Trent. 'Such a waste. If later you become lonely, you only have to lift the phone. Weldon will answer, but you can ask to be put through to me.'

'I hardly think it will be necessary,' Felicity told him. 'And please don't bother about me tomorrow morning. If I may use the phone to call a cab, I can be gone before you wake.'

His smile was ironic.

'Oh, Felicity, do you really believe you can get away from me so easily? I'll leave you now because you say you wish it, though I can't believe you really do deep in that heart of yours. I have a date with my driver right now, but I'll come back later to find out whether I can change your mind. If the door is locked, I'll know the answer is "no", but please don't let it be.'

He walked towards the door with the lithe stride of some wild animal and then he turned. His green-gold eyes swept over her, magnetic, disturbing, and she felt naked under his gaze.

'I've always found that it's the things I don't experience that I regret—and take it from me, you'll always wonder what this night could have been like. So think about it carefully but not too carefully, and perhaps you'll change your mind. I'm sure I could easily change it for you, but I want your full consent, and maybe I'll get it before this night is out. Here's hoping!'

And with that he was gone. Felicity heard those padding panther-like steps receding along the corridor and now she was alone. Alone with her thoughts. What had happened to her? The violent emotion that was troubling her even now had never come to her before. You can't have such feelings for a stranger, she thought. Have some sense, Felicity. He's obviously a man who's easily attracted to women and is used to them falling for him just as easily. It's ridiculous. He isn't the type of man that you can even like. You were thrown together by pure chance and he wants to snatch the opportunity to make love to you, because he likes the look of you and you would gratify his conceit. What's more, he's a very rich man and your lives would never cross each other's path again. I guess that makes it safe for him. But what about me?

She put her hand to her mouth that still burned from the violence of his kisses. When he comes back . . .? she thought. He's made his intentions plain, and if he kisses me again, how do I know I'll have the strength to resist him? And in a blind panic she decided, I mustn't let that happen. I must go and never see him again.

Hastily she dressed again in her blue uniform. Smoothing back her hair under the neat cap, she looked in the mirror and was glad to see that she looked a different person once more. This is me, she thought, not that passionate woman in the satin robe. She lifted the phone, dreading that she might still hear Trent's low vibrant tones, but Weldon answered her.

'Weldon, I've decided I should go tonight instead of in the morning. Do you think you could call a cab for me and help me to negotiate the elevator?'

There was a long pause.

'Does Mr Seymour know you're going, miss?'

For once Felicity felt that a lie was justified.

'Yes, I discussed it with him. We agreed that I should go as soon as I was ready.'

'He didn't tell me, but he said you might call later. Very well, miss, I'll come to fetch your bags.'

It was possible that Weldon approved of her decision to go. In any case, he did not make things difficult for her.

She was terrified that she might meet Trent when Weldon had taken her to the top of the cliff, but there was no sign of him and the manservant helped her into the cab and gave instructions to the driver.

'Thank you, Weldon, and please say goodbye to Mr Seymour for me.'

'You're welcome. I'll do that, miss.'

There was almost a smile on his monkey face as the cab drew away from the kerb. Felicity sank back on the seat and tried to look ahead to the morning when she must start the new job. She must forget all about Trent, because she would never see him again.

CHAPTER THREE

THE huge hotel by the waterfront seemed stark and impersonal after the warm luxury of Trent's house, but nevertheless Felicity sought refuge in her tenth floor room like a bird that has escaped from its elaborate gilded cage. In spite of her agitation, she was so exhausted that she managed to snatch a few hours' sleep. Trent knew where she would be staying and she half hoped, half dreaded he would call her, but there was no word from him and she resolutely put all thought of him behind and tried to concentrate on her arrangements for the tour. The next morning, as soon as she could, she phoned the office and arranged to go over to tie up all the last-minute details. She was to meet her party in the afternoon and take them by coach to get the ferry which would convey them across the water to Victoria on Vancouver Island.

The crowd in the office were very friendly and welcoming, and soon she was shown into a room to meet a senior member of the staff.

'Hi, Felicity, glad to know you. I'm here to brief you on the tour. I understand it's your first one in these parts.'

'Yes, I'm looking forward to it tremendously. I haven't done it before, but they told me in Montreal that I was to be with a very experienced driver.'

'Ah, yes, that was so until yesterday. However, there's been a hitch. But not to worry, I'm here to give you all the information I can in as short a time as possible.'

'A hitch?' she queried.

'Yes, the driver who was to come with you has had some family trouble and he's pulled out of the tour, but he's found a substitute, a man not up to now on our payroll, but I'm told he's a very good driver and knows the country. It's too bad this had to happen on your first tour, but I'm sure you'll manage very well. Unfortunately none of our regular drivers were available, but Scotty wouldn't just send us anyone. He knows how important it is.'

'Oh, that's disappointing,' agreed Felicity, 'but I've studied this tour pretty extensively. I guess if you set me down anywhere on the route I could take a guess at my location. Not to worry, I'm determined to make everyone happy, including myself.'

'That's grand. Now let's get down to work. There's one thing that's fortunate—you haven't got a full coach, so everyone will have room to stretch. But remember, when a group is smaller it's all the more important that everyone should get on well together, and a lot of that side of it's up to you.'

For the next couple of hours Felicity was briefed on all aspects of the journey, and by the time her tutor relented enough to send out for a salad and doughnuts and coffee for lunch, she felt thoroughly knowledgeable about the work she had to do.

'Keep them happy, that's the main thing,' she was told. 'But be firm. Don't let yourself be scared by any of these old dragons who sometimes turn up on vacation. On the other hand don't, for heaven's sake, let yourself get involved romantically with any member of the tour. That leads to far too many complications, take it from me.'

'I won't,' Felicity promised hastily.

After last night, there's no way I want romance, she thought. But I don't expect to meet another Trent on this tour; I guess they don't come too often. And in spite of everything, she felt an uneasy, uncomfortable emotion of regret. I'll see him no more, she thought, and I don't think I'll ever meet anyone like him again. He's the sort of man who makes you think God broke the pattern when he made him. Maybe it's just as well too. I must put him right out of my mind.

'I've arranged for the driver to bring the coach around to the front of your hotel where your guests have been told to assemble at thirty after four,' said her colleague. 'You'll have a little time to chat first before the coach arrives and then you'll board the ferry for the crossing to Victoria. But we've been over all this before. You know the schedule and all that remains is to wish you the best of luck on your first trip. You understand this is a trial run for you and if you satisfy the customers then the job will be permanent. I hope everything goes well, but after meeting you, I feel sure that you'll have no hassles, and if you do you seem very competent to solve them.'

Felicity was glad she had managed to inspire confidence in his mind, but she felt a little nervous at the thought that she was going to have to cover entirely new ground and without the experienced driver she had expected. Ah, well, it couldn't be helped.

She collected her uniform that had been dry-cleaned and, returning to her hotel room, she bathed and changed into it. It had suffered no lasting damage, and when she looked at herself in the mirror she was pleased to see that her usual image had been restored. She looked the neat, competent courier. Her red-gold hair was tamed into a sedate knot beneath the rather impudent tilt of the blue forage cap that matched the deep blue of her eyes, and her safari-type jacket with its shining silver buttons was belted over a paler blue shirt that was buttoned high at the neck. A pleated skirt and flat lace-up navy Oxfords completed the impression of someone very far removed from that reflection in the mirror of Trent's rose-coloured room.

At four she descended to the ground floor and, after ordering a cup of coffee, took up a position at a corner table where she could watch her guests arrive but not yet be seen herself. It would be interesting to try to put names to them from her list before she had actually met them. Those two women, bronzed and outdoor types, they had to be the two Australians. They looked pleasant enough and efficient too with their neat small suitcases and their travel bags slung over their shoulders. Medium brown hair, pleated skirts, one navy with a red blazer, the other cream with a brown blazer. They seemed sociable, for they had already started to chat to another tourist, this time a man, tall rangy frame, dark blond hair, fair beard, grey-blue safari suit. Could he be the Norwegian in the party? Olaf Gustaffsen—that must be he.

Here came some more, hesitating at first, and then, with the encouragement of the Australians, joining the group, a young couple casually dressed in jeans and matching T-shirts of bright red, each printed with their name. Al and Mary Lou. They had arms intertwined even while they were talking to the strangers and could not seem to keep their eyes off each other. As more people came to join the original group, Felicity thought it was time she made herself known to them. It was a little like being a teacher, she thought, as she crossed the names off her register. And the new pupils? Some of them were polite, others a little brash, all somewhat awkward, possibly sizing each other up and wondering what it would be like to spend two weeks in this company.

Edith and Anne Bowden, the Australians, were useful immediately, chatting to all the others, putting people at their ease. Felicity could see she was going to be grateful to them. Al Draper and Mary Lou Todd confessed shyly that they had just graduated and had become engaged. Their trip was a present paid for by their parents, who had promised it if they achieved good grades.

Yes, the man with the golden beard was Olaf Gustaffsen, just as she had thought. He examined Felicity with direct sea-blue eyes and shook her by the hand in a grasp that was firm and sure. There were others in the party, a middle-aged couple from England, several people from Holland, some Canadians, naturally, but she would have time to disentangle the others later in her mind. At this moment she must make sure they were all here, for the coach was due at any moment and they must not keep it waiting as it was only allowed to stand in front of the hotel for the limited period that it took to load passengers and baggage. She went through the list again. Was anyone missing? Ah, yes, Crystal and Denise Harcourt, mother and daughter, address, New York. She hoped they would arrive soon. So far everything seemed to be going smoothly and none of her guests looked very autocratic or terrifying on this short acquaintance. It would be too bad now if they had to delay the coach because of the non-arrival of the Harcourts.

And here was the porter coming towards them to tell them that the coach had arrived. Well, she would have to start loading the passengers and their baggage without the missing women. Inwardly worried, but trying not to show it, she smilingly ushered her little flock of passengers towards the swing doors at the entrance of the hotel. And there was the coach, bright blue and shining, with huge windows for viewing and a look of luxury that should please the travellers. Felicity looked curiously at her driver. He had descended from the high seat and was helping the porter to stack the mound of baggage into the cavernous compartment below the coach. His back was towards her, but she thought that at least he looked a strong man, the way he was handling the cases as if they were merely lunch boxes. The pale blue of his uniform jacket enhanced the breadth of his shoulders and, beneath the blue forage cap similar to her own, there sprang a thick growth of dark wavy hair. Oh, heavens, where had she seen those strong brown hands before? It couldn't be . . . she must be imagining this!

But it was. He turned and she was looking again at eyes that were green flecked with gold and a mouth that she remembered only too well.

'Hi, Felicity,' he said cheerfully. 'Nice to meet you again. It seems we're going to see a lot of each other for the next fortnight, doesn't it?'

'But you can't . . .' she stuttered. 'You can't be coming! They said they would send an experienced driver.'

'And so I am. I told you I'd driven heavy duty vehicles in less prosperous days, and that was not so very long ago. Try to look a little more welcoming to your fellow workmate, Felicity, or else the passengers will begin to be uneasy. Everything must appear smooth even if it isn't, as you, as an experienced courier, should know. Don't worry, I can drive a coach very adequately and I'll explain how it happened later. Just now our duty is with our customers. Time's running on and we must get them to the ferry. Don't look so stricken, for pity's sake. There's nothing you can do about it, so look cheerful.'

Felicity felt stunned, but she dazedly went through the motions of settling everyone comfortably in their seats and explaining the procedure that they would follow at the ferry, and her mind was distracted still further by the arrival of Crystal and Denise Harcourt, who stepped out of their cab with what seemed to Felicity to be a mountain of baggage. They might be mother and daughter, but they were totally different in their appearance. The older one of the two had shining black hair beneath a chic hat of purple satin with a small veil that seemed to enhance her huge, luminous violet eyes. She was wearing a suit of beautiful soft heather wool and carried a wrap of silver-grey fox—not very suitable gear for this kind of tour, Felicity thought, more the kind you would wear for a morning's shopping on Fifth Avenue. But everything she had seemed exquisite, the Gucci shoes and bag of soft leather, the gold chains on her neck and wrists. The initials on her bag read 'C.H.', so this must be Crystal Harcourt and the daughter must be Denise. Denise was something else again— long blonde hair almost waist length, huge brown eyes, casual clothes, the kind that look almost shabby but cost the earth, cream cord jeans with the label of a distinguished couturier on the small perfect bottom, a chamois vest and a bronze leather jacket with matching flat leather pumps on the slender feet.

There was no apology for the lateness of their arrival. They were the kind of women, Felicity thought, who would always behave as if they owned the earth.

'We must have the front seats,' Crystal informed

Felicity. 'My daughter can't bear to have to look at other people's heads.'

'The coach is built to give everyone the best of views, Mrs Harcourt,' Felicity said mildly. 'And we make it a rule on these tours that everyone moves around each day so that they all get a turn at the front seats.'

'Is that right? They didn't tell me that when I booked. I thought I made it plain to them that we should have front seats all the time.'

Trouble, thought Felicity, and, as she looked at Denise's sulky, beautiful mouth, double trouble, in fact.

'Have our seat. We really don't mind where we sit, do we, Al?'

It was Mary Lou speaking, and, before Felicity could protest, Denise had slipped into the proffered seat and Crystal was accepting Trent's help in disposing of her fur and overnight bag on the rack above. They were much more gracious with Trent than they had been with her, Felicity noticed. She felt annoyed with herself that she had not been more firm about insisting on the young couple keeping their seats. Ah well, it was early days yet—but she would have to see that the Harcourts didn't get all the advantages that they obviously thought were their due at the expense of the other travellers. She felt even more ruffled now. What could have brought Trent to be working as a driver of her coach? And there was nothing to be done at the moment save to put a good face on it; no time for discussion. All her duty lay with the passengers.

The coach drew away smoothly from the front of the bayside hotel and very soon they were driving south out of Vancouver and across the long bridge over the mighty Fraser River with its busy traffic of ships, then into flat farmlands. Not very interesting, this first part of the journey, but the passengers were making tentative rapprochements to each other and for once were not concerned with the scenery. Felicity felt she could leave them to themselves for the moment and go to tackle Trent. She went to sit at the small seat that was left for her behind the driver.

'What are you doing on my coach?' she asked fiercely.

'Driving it,' he replied.

He smiled without taking his eyes from the road. How smug he looked! thought Felicity. She felt a wave of pure hatred flowing through her veins. That false attraction of the previous night had vanished with the dawn.

'It's no laughing matter,' she said angrily. 'How did you get here?'

'Hold your horses, Felicity. I've told you, there'll be time for explanations later. At the moment all I'm concerned with is getting your passengers safely to the ferry. A big girl like you should be able to read. What does the notice in front of you say?'

There was the usual sort of print-out warning passengers not to talk to the driver when the coach was in motion. Felicity gave an exasperated exclamation.

'You're impossible, but don't think I'm going to stand for this. They'll have to send me another driver.'

'Quiet, Felicity. Go and chat to the customers. Look after them and I'll look after the driving. That's what we're being paid for. When we arrive at the ferry, leave everything to me. We can argue later.'

She sat quietly in her seat, but inwardly she was fuming. What were Trent's intentions? She could not believe that he really meant to keep up this masquerade for two whole weeks. She supposed it all seemed like a huge joke to him, but on the success of this tour depended her whole career. What was to happen? Everything seemed to have gone wrong the moment Wyatt had called for her in Montreal. Wyatt? She had not given him another thought since she had left him so abruptly on the road to the airport. She must call him some time, because he didn't even know her address. Across her thoughts she was aware that Crystal and Denise Harcourt were talking to each other.

'Are you comfortable, Denise honey?'

'Not so that you'd notice. Of all the dumb ideas that Pop ever had it was sending us on this trip. Don't think I don't know why he did it—it was to get me away from all my crowd. But if he thinks he can improve me by making me mix with all these dumb types on this coach, he's very much mistaken.'

'Don't be like that, Denise. I didn't want to come here any more than you did. I'd far rather have gone to Miami Beach, but Daddy thought you should see this part of the world. I guess he thought it might improve your class marks if you knew more about this country near to the United States.'

'I don't want to improve my class marks. What's the need for good grades when I'm going to be a fashion model or get in the movies? Anyhow, I didn't know you were all that set on what Daddy wants. You're divorced from him, aren't you?'

'Sure I'm divorced, but he still thinks he has a say in what you do.'

'I don't see why. Just because he pays you a large alimony, it doesn't mean he can rule my life.'

There was silence for a few moments, then Denise said, 'Say, will you just take a look at that driver? He looks like he could be in movies too. Did you ever see a more rugged type? He'd look great in Westerns.'

'Oh, yeah, he sure is easy on the eye. I noticed him the moment he started to stack our bags. He certainly has something going for him.'

Denise's voice, though petulant, had been direct and childish, but Felicity noticed that Crystal's had a kind of sensuality in its purring tones. She was startled to feel a swift stab of emotion. Not jealousy, surely? No, it couldn't be. It was just that she was worried and unsettled by Trent's presence as well as the thought that these two females, lovely as they were, could introduce a disturbing element into the tour.

In spite of her reservations about Trent's ability as a driver and fellow worker for this tour, she had to admit that he behaved with perfect efficiency when they arrived at the ferry. The coach was swiftly stowed away into the great yawning depths of the ship and the passengers climbed down with courteous assistance from Trent.

'You'll be able to get something to eat on board. It takes over an hour and a half to arrive at Swartz Bay. Get down here again when you hear an announcement over the loudspeaker. Please don't be late, because we mustn't hold things up.'

She watched the passengers ascending the metal staircase that led to the more habitable quarters of the ship. Trent was locking the doors of the coach. At least he seemed to know what was required of him—but oh, what was he doing here? She had been used on the previous tours she had undertaken in the East to having a companionable relationship with her driver with no emotional involvement, and now she hated the whole idea of making this tour, the tour that was new to her, and on which so much depended in the company of this man, a stranger but one with whom she had felt unable to cope after a few short hours in his company.

'Well now, how about our getting some food ourselves?' asked Trent. 'We've done our duty by the customers for a while, let's make the most of this break.'

'Are you already getting tired of being a driver?' she asked.

'Not at all, so don't sound so hopeful, Felicity. This has been a heaven-sent opportunity for me and I'm going to make the most of it, you can be sure, in more ways than one.'

She wanted to shrug off the strong grasp of that muscular arm as he guided her up the stairway, but he held her firmly.

'Sit down while I catch a snack for us,' he commanded. 'This is amusing. I haven't had to queue for a meal in years.'

He strode off in the direction of the self-service restaurant with not even an enquiry concerning her wishes.

'How do you know I'm not allergic to seafood?' Felicity asked him when he returned with bowls of clam chowder and plates of shrimp salad.

'I trusted to my judgment. You look very healthy. You don't have any allergies, do you?'

'Only to men like you.'

'In that case, you can't suffer much, because you won't meet anyone else like me. And you look remarkably well in my company—now admit it.'

He was pouring white wine into her glass and she thought how familiar those long brown hands seemed to her after such a short time. She tried not to respond to his smile.

'I think you owe me an explanation,' she said.

'Simple, my dear Felicity. My driver and I have this date playing poker whenever I come to Vancouver. Other drivers join in, so he has a working acquaintance with things that are going on in the city. Last night someone called him to ask if he knew of an available driver for this tour. They'd been phoning all around because the man who should have been with you had domestic trouble. His wife is having a baby and has had to go to hospital with some complication.'

'But that doesn't explain how you . . .?'

'It came to me in a flash. I'd been saying to you how much I'd enjoy getting away from it all, and here was the perfect opportunity. I realised that it might be your tour, the same company and only one coach leaving today. Frankly I thought you'd be delighted with the idea. It seemed fate was being very generous to both of us.'

'You may think so, but I don't,' she told him sharply.

'No need to be churlish, Felicity—that means happiness, doesn't it? Just think how much happiness we could have together. Two whole weeks of your life, Felicity, never to be forgotten.'

'I thought I'd made it clear last night what I thought of your ideas of happiness.'

'Ah, yes, Weldon let me know you'd left, but I knew you couldn't get far, and you see how right I was, because here we are, the two of us, all set for a delightful tour together.'

'I don't see anything of the kind. I don't understand you, Trent. You helped me to get to this job on time and now you seem determined to wreck my chances. I can't work properly with someone like you around. I can't give of my best to the tour. What do you want? Why have you followed me?'

'I think you know what I want and, as I told you last night, I'm used to getting it too. But don't worry about this job of yours. It's perfectly safe. I'll be very well behaved, I promise you, during the day. I'll help you all I can. When I set my mind to doing anything well, whether it's driving a coach, assisting as a courier, or, shall we whisper it? making love to a beautiful girl, there's no holding me.'

Felicity sighed in exasperation.

'I never before met any man with such an exaggerated opinion of himself! You're quite impossible. As soon as we get to Victoria I intend to phone and ask for another driver.'

'I shouldn't do that if I were you,' said Trent. 'Just think, you are new here and, if you say you can't get on with the first driver they give you, what kind of impression will that make? No, Felicity, like it or not, it looks like you're stuck with me for a fortnight. Finished your coffee? So let's take a turn around the deck before you get tied up with our customers again. I can see my opportunities will be few and far between on this trip and I'll have to make the most of them.'

Before she could make any protest, he had whisked her out of the saloon and on to the narrow open deck. In the blueness of evening, shapes of islands loomed around them as the ship was guided through the narrow channel, its water flowing fast on an out-running tide. A white seabird shouted harshly and flew away from its perch on the rail. They were the only passengers out on deck, and Felicity thought that the saloon they had left looked infinitely warm and inviting, casting out its golden glow into the darkening waves. Again she felt that shadow of fear at being alone with Trent, this determined man who seemed to get his own way in all things, and she wished she had never met him. And yet some part of her was deeply affected by the haunting, lonely scene, the blue of the islands, the pewter water and this man at her side, holding her close against him, sheltering her from the chill wind. She had thought he might try to kiss her and some stranger inside herself half yearned for it to happen, but he did not, and they stood for a long time locked together like lovers by the strength of the wind and watching the turbulent wake of the ship stretching out behind them.

'Back to work,' said Trent at last. 'It's time to call the passengers. This has been a delightful interlude, Felicity. I hope there are going to be many more like it.'

'Not if I can help it,' said Felicity.

CHAPTER FOUR

THEY were to spend two nights in the city of Victoria before setting out upon the journey proper.

'You'll find that the tour begins to jell properly after you've completed the first couple of days,' the tour operator had advised her, and Felicity hoped he was right. For her it had begun to unjell the moment she had recognised the driver. But perhaps she could keep him at a distance by becoming especially concerned with her passengers. Therefore she encouraged them in his hearing to come to her room if they had any queries and so she spent the first evening in conversation, getting to know them better. She knew that Trent had gone off to see to the fuelling and proper preparation of the coach and she hoped he would be fully occupied with this.

She did not see him again until the next morning when there he was at nine o'clock sharp waiting with the coach in front of the hotel and looking smart as a student prince in his blue uniform that seemed to emphasise the deep bronze of his face and hands. It annoyed Felicity somehow to see him in this get-up. It was too much a reminder of his masquerade.

'When we've left Victoria, you don't have to wear uniform all the time,' she told him. 'During the other part of the tour we're allowed to be informal, just so long as we look neat and tidy. That's what it says in the rules.'

'Thank you for telling me. I'll remember that.'

Felicity looked at him suspiciously. There was a hint of a smile about the curving mouth, that mouth that could look cruel on occasion but had a strong sensuality about the lower lip.

'We must always be careful to abide by the rules, mustn't we, Miss Tait?' he added.

She ignored this and went to speak to one of the passengers. I suppose I did sound like a schoolmistress, she thought, but I wish he didn't have the power to rile me so much. As she picked up the loudspeaker, she was conscious of the fact that he was listening—listening and probably criticising. Crystal and Denise Harcourt were in the front seat again. Well, this time it didn't really matter. The Butchart Gardens to which they were heading was at Tod Inlet, only a matter of thirteen miles from the city of Victoria.

'Started by Mrs Butchart who objected to her husband's abandoned limestone quarry that she could see from her house, it's now the outstanding showplace of the Pacific Northwest,' she told her passengers. 'You'll be shown around the place by one of the staff and then you'll be free to wander about on your own, but please see that you're back at the coach by half past twelve.'

Denise Harcourt gave a loud, affected yawn.

'All this regimentation is so boring,' she told her mother in a voice that could be heard the whole length of the coach.

'We try not to overdo it,' said Felicity in what she hoped was a pleasant voice. 'But some acceptance of the limitations of a tour with other people is rather necessary, don't you think?'

She moved along to speak to the other passengers.

'What nonsense,' said Edith Bowden. 'If they didn't want to be limited about time, why didn't they hire their own car, and why be so damned rude?'

'She's young,' said Felicity, 'and doesn't like to be restricted. She'll settle down, no doubt.'

'I wonder,' said Edith. 'Those two behave as if they own the coach. They're too used to getting their own way, if you ask me.'

That makes three of them then, thought Felicity, for certainly the same could apply to Trent. When she came up front, she glanced at his arrogant profile. Although his eyes were on the road, he knew she was there.

'I'm taking the scenic route,' he said. 'That's all right with you, madam?'

'A good idea. It takes us off the main highway.'

'I'm glad you think some of my ideas are good. How about having dinner with me tonight?'

'It's too early to think about dinner. Besides, I might be involved with the customers, as you call them.'

'Give them a break, can't you? They have you around all day. They can't expect to have you around all night too.'

But you can, thought Felicity. Oh, no, Trent. I'm going to be very careful to avoid your company when the others are not around.

There was a feeling of late spring in the air and the bushes of dogwood were still starry with white blossoms as they passed through pretty wooded country with quite large clearings surrounding small houses.

'I'm told land used to be quite cheap here,' she told the tourists, 'but now that they have found it's profitable to supply vegetables to the city, it's become expensive to buy it.'

'Where did you learn that?' asked Trent. 'You're quite a mine of information, aren't you?'

'I swotted it up beforehand. I've done a lot of hard work on this tour—I told you I want it to be a success. I can't have it ruined by you or anyone else. This is a trial run, so to speak. If I flop, I'm out and I don't want to fail. I want to stay here and go on working for this company. If they throw me out, I won't get another job of this kind anywhere in British Columbia.'

But you couldn't worry about that, she thought bitterly. This is all a big joke to you. You took over this driving job just for the laughs and now I'm stuck with you. I could almost hate you for that, Trent Seymour. But she didn't say it aloud. It would not improve her tour to make the driver angry, now would it?

'The estate is called Benvenuto—Welcome,' she told her passengers now. 'A lovely name for a lovely place.'

Trent parked the coach with his usual accuracy and the passengers disembarked.

'Let them get lost for a while, when you've arranged for their guide,' he advised. 'You don't need to be their nursemaid. It's a heavenly day. How about doing the gardens with me?'

Felicity looked at him. She thought she should beware of that charming, wicked smile, and yet what harm could come to her in these gardens, crowded as they were with a thousand visitors? She shepherded her charges off with the guide and returned to find him equipped with two cups of coffee.

'All that lecturing must make you dry,' he remarked. 'Come along, drink up and I'll show you the gardens. It'll be a nice change for you to be guided.'

'Have you been here before?' she asked.

'Certainly. I've been to most places in my life. Come along. Our passengers have had a head start, no risk of catching up with them now.'

He put his arm around her to guide her down the

path away from the coffee bar. She had discarded her
jacket because the day was warm and now she was
too conscious of his hand at her waist, strong and
pliable through the thin cotton of her blue shirt. The
curving path, edged with pink and blue viscaria, led
through rambling roses festooned upon pillars and,
in the background, the dogwood still showed some of
its blossom.

'We should have come earlier,' Trent told her. 'In
spring there are tulips and wallflowers over a carpet
of pink and blue forget-me-nots.'

He would not have come by himself, she thought.
With what other woman had he wandered in this
heavenly place? The one he said he had loved all his
life? Could she be married to someone else? But
even if he did love her, he didn't appear to be very
faithful to her, did he? There was a kind of bower by
the side of the path, hung with baskets, each one
filled to the brim with an opulent display of fuchsias
and begonias in bright crimsons and shades of pink,
and Trent drew her aside into this place so that she
felt herself surrounded by glowing colours on every
side.

'What a pity your hair has to be bound up in
that . . . what do you call it? . . . French pleat. I'd
like to see it down on your shoulders, red-gold
against that brilliant contrast of pinks and reds.'

His hand was still at her waist, but his other hand
reached up and smoothed the silky texture of her
hair, then caressed her cheek before holding her
chin so that she was forced to meet those golden
mocking eyes.

'People will see us,' she protested weakly.

There were many visitors and they could hear
their voices quite near on the path beside the bower.

'A man admiring a pretty girl shouldn't surprise
them. Many lovers must come to this garden,

wouldn't you think so, Felicity?'

'But we're not lovers,' she pointed out.

'Unfortunately, no, and there are far too many people around for me to persuade you otherwise. We'll continue our tour, shall we?'

Others had come into their flowering recess and Felicity was surprised by a fleeting sensation of disappointment. But she could not truly want to be alone with him, could she?

'The sunken garden next,' Trent told her. 'I like to think of Mrs. Butchart, when she was well over fifty, hanging in a bosun's chair planting ivy and Virginia creeper in its rocky walls, because this used to be the limestone quarry and the garden had to be landscaped from very uncompromising material.'

'It looks wonderful now,' said Felicity.

They had climbed up some steps and now stood above the sunken garden which lay fifty feet below them, ablaze with bright flowers.

'What are those dark, beautifully shaped trees?' she asked.

'They're called the Tree of Life. They don't have to be trimmed, they just grow in that natural shape with dense foliage.'

'They certainly look very vital.'

And the man at her side looked very vital too, she thought. He was the kind of person that others noticed, and she was conscious of other women's glances as, having descended the steps, they passed through the lovely garden so abounding with stocks, potentilla, aquilegia, myosotis, so bright with flowering trees and shrubs, it seemed impossible to take it all in. Beyond the Trees of Life, beyond the Japanese cherry trees, the path wound on, coming to an open stretch of lawn with a towering rock and on the left a silvery waterfall starting from the very top of the cliff and falling into a stream that eventually found its way to a lake, the edge of which was planted with maple and more flowering cherry. They paused on the other side of the lake and all around them the lovely trees were reflected in the still water.

'It's such a wonderful place,' said Felicity. 'Oh, do look at that statue of a young girl with the weeping birch beside her. To create a garden like this out of ugliness—what an achievement! I'd rather have done that than have all the money in the world.'

'But Mrs Butchart could hardly have done it without money, and now it needs money to keep it going. Nothing can be done without money, you'll find, Felicity,' Trent remarked drily.

But she would not let him annoy her, she thought. The sun shone warm out of a clear blue sky, ruffled only by small white clouds, and she felt that her tour must go well and hoped her tourists were enjoying this beautiful place as much as she was. They paused on the bridge to observe the fountain spurting seventy feet into the air from its place in the water below, constantly changing its pattern.

'It looks quite magnificent at night,' Trent told her. 'It's illuminated with brilliant variations of coloured lights.'

With whom had he stood on this bridge overlooking the cascading water on some enchanted evening not so long ago?

'It must be a very romantic spot at that time,' she remarked.

'Yes, indeed, very exciting, especially if you happen to be in the right sort of company.'

I expect he was, thought Felicity.

'What's that frown in aid of?' she heard him say. 'How can I convince you, Felicity, that this next two weeks could be a high spot in both our lives? Relax, girl, and think of it that way.'

'And how can I convince you, Trent, that the next two weeks are very important in my life but not for the reason you mean? I want this tour to go properly, and I'm not in the least concerned with anything else. I've somehow got to get through the tour with you as my driver, but don't think there's going to be anything else between us, because there's not. No way.'

'What a pity this garden is so crowded with visitors,' he observed. 'If I had you alone what would you like to bet I could convince you otherwise in sixty seconds?'

'I never bet,' Felicity answered.

'You'd lose,' Trent told her.

They were passing through a rioting splendour of roses, their fragrance strangely intermingled with the acrid smell of English boxwood. Delphiniums, as blue as the sky, and white and magenta foxgloves raised their tall spires with more roses in foaming waves of colour upon the arches above them. Then past another fountain, adorned with bronze dolphins, and under maples and japonica to the descending path by the winding pools of the Japanese garden with its weeping willows and dwarf trees and strangely shaped shrubs, its lacquered bridge and small summerhouses. Below them was the bay glimpsed occasionally through the trees.

'Now what do you say to sitting in one of those teahouses and admiring the view for a while?' said Trent, putting his arm through hers and drawing her towards one of the little buildings in the middle of the miniature lake.

'There isn't time, Trent, we must get back. It will take us half an hour or more and I mustn't fail my own deadline, must I?'

'Too bad,' drawled Trent. 'I begin to see disadvantages in this mode of travel. However, I promised to behave myself during the day, didn't I? So come on, let's go.'

Now he strode on ahead and she had a hard time keeping up with him. She wondered if he was displeased with her or if he was regretting the whole thing—his involvement in the tour, the wild masquerade. She was sure he had done it on an impulse and would soon begin to regret it, especially if his threatened pursuit of her brought him no results. Well, whose fault was it anyway? she thought rebelliously, as she rushed breathlessly after him through the Italian garden with its mermaid fountain.

Back at the coach, she found Edith and Anne Bowden trying to calm an hysterical Crystal Harcourt.

'She was with me one moment and then she disappeared. I can't understand it. Oh, where can she be?'

'She's lost Denise, her daughter,' muttered Edith to Felicity. 'She's sure to turn up soon, but meanwhile she's going frantic. You sure got yourself a load of trouble with this one!'

Trent stepped forward and put a large reassuring hand on Crystal's shoulder. She turned to him and her lovely eyes, spilling over with tears, looked like dew-wet violets.

'Please find her for me! Oh, I know you can find her, Mr . . .'

'Call me Trent,' he told her. 'Stop worrying, Mrs Harcourt, I'll find her.'

'You're so very kind, Trent. Is that your first name?' She put her hand in his in a confiding gesture.

'Yes, madam. Now where did you see her last?'

'In the rose garden. She said she was bored and the next thing she was gone. Oh, heavens, do you

suppose she's fallen into the lake or off one of those
bridges?'

'Highly unlikely, and if she had, there'd be hundreds of people around to rescue her. I'll go search
for her, but I don't think I'll have to go far.'

He was away, his long legs striding out as he left
the parking ground. Felicity could hear the other
passengers grumbling a little. They had had a long,
rather tiring morning and now they wanted to get
back to lunch as soon as possible.

'How long do you think we'll take to get back to
Victoria?' one couple asked her. 'We have a date
with some friends and we haven't seen them for ages.'

'I'm so sorry, but we'll have to wait,' said Felicity.
'We can't go with Denise missing.'

It was not very long afterwards that Trent arrived
back with the girl. She was not in the least apolo-
getic about keeping everyone waiting. Indeed, she
seemed pleased to be the centre of attention and, as
Trent hurried her along, she chatted to him, looking
up into his face with a devastating, wide smile.

'Doesn't that slay you?' muttered Edith. 'She
keeps everyone waiting and now she's trying to do a
big glamour act on your driver!'

Denise looked bored when Crystal reproached her
for her disappearance.

'The gardens were such a drag. I found a gang in
the coffee bar who were practising their guitars. It
was real cool. We were having a ball until one of the
wardens stopped us.'

As they climbed back into the coach, Edith
Bowden said to Felicity, 'Join us for dinner tonight if
you aren't doing anything else.'

'Thanks, I'd love to,' she smiled.

This way she would avoid an encounter with
Trent. It was true he had asked her first, but she had
not accepted. You must play safe, she told herself.

No romantic evenings with him. He only promised to behave during the day. So don't say you haven't been warned. But he didn't repeat his invitation and, when Felicity joined the two Australian women in the dining room on the top floor of the hotel, she saw that Trent was there at a nearby table in the company of Crystal and Denise Harcourt, and seemed to be getting on with them extremely well.

'Those man-eaters have got their claws into your driver, Felicity,' said Edith, laughing.

'I think he's quite capable of looking after himself,' Felicity replied.

'He looks it. I could go for him myself, couldn't you, Anne?'

'Not my type. I prefer fair men. How about asking Mr Gustaffsen to share our meal? He's just come in on his own.'

Nothing loath, Edith went to where the big Scandinavian was waiting to be directed to a table, and he smiled and came over to join them. He was a very handsome man in a way totally different from Trent's rugged good looks, although he too looked an outdoor type with his golden skin, vividly blue eyes, golden beard and curly dark blond hair. He spoke English remarkably well, as most of his countrymen do, and he regarded Felicity with open admiration, insisting on treating the company to a light, sparkling wine to celebrate their first dinner together.

'*Skol.* May we have a trouble-free tour. But how can we have anything else with such a charming hostess?'

There was much laughter and pleasant chat at their table, but presently, when the meal was over, Edith and Anne Bowden excused themselves.

'We must catch up on sleep for our early start tomorrow.'

Felicity rose to go too, but Olaf protested.

'Stay a while longer. I'd like to ask you some things about the tour. I may not get the opportunity, because you will have a crowd around you tomorrow.'

But when she had settled down again, he didn't seem in a hurry to ask his questions. He ordered more coffee and this came with thin peppermint candies. The restaurant was high above the city, and a carpet of lights was spread below them.

'During the day you can see right over to the Olympic mountains in Washington State,' Felicity told him, 'across the Juan de Fuca Strait. I think there's snow on the mountains. What a pity you can't see them now.'

'My view is good enough here. I'm not complaining,' said Olaf.

He was looking only at her. Oh, dear, thought Felicity. No romantic complications! She looked away from him and caught sight of Trent glancing in her direction. He must have noticed how Olaf's attention was concentrated so obviously on her, for his smile was mocking as if he were enjoying some private joke. Then he turned back to Crystal and Denise, who seemed to be vying for his attention. Nor did he seem to be hating it, thought Felicity. Well, perhaps that solved her problem. She turned to Olaf and gave him a charming smile.

'What was it you wanted to know about the tour?' she asked. 'I'm here to give you as much help as I can. Feel free to ask me, if you have any problems.'

'I'll remember that,' said the handsome Scandinavian.

He put out one brown hand and pressed hers. She did not withdraw it, but all the time she was conscious of those gold-green eyes at the other table, mocking her.

CHAPTER FIVE

NEXT morning Felicity was up bright and early, because she felt everything depended on how the tour was to go now that they were setting off from Victoria, from the city to the wilderness. Up to now everything that had happened was in sophisticated surroundings, but from now on the setting of the tour would be foreign to most of the tourists, and if they were to get the most enjoyment out of it, a lot depended on their courier.

However, she was not much earlier than Trent, who came and sat down at her table in the restaurant without so much as asking her permission. It was a table for two in the same high place where they had been last night. But now you could see the whole wide landscape of town and ocean spread out below, a marvellous view right over to the snow-capped Mount Olympus in the United States over the Strait of Juan de Fuca. The scene was bathed in early morning sunshine, the sky a brilliant blue, with clouds sailing in the azure air, the same odd shape that they would have been in a child's drawing.

Trent eyed her helping of bacon, her egg sunny side up, the pyramid of small pancakes covered with maple syrup and the cup of strong coffee.

'Bring me the same,' he ordered, 'but make it two eggs. I like a girl with a good appetite, and you'll need plenty of nourishment today, won't you, Felicity? It's all go from now on, I gather.'

'It certainly seems so,' she agreed.

'Well, the route's pretty straightforward and the coach is all ready. And the passengers you have got

seem docile enough. Your handsome Norwegian is
eating out of your hand already.'

Felicity looked across and caught the mocking
glance of those gold-green eyes beneath the thickly
arched dark eyebrows.

'You don't seem to be doing too badly yourself,'
she retorted.

'Must keep the customers amused,' he said.

I suppose Crystal and Denise are having breakfast
in their room, thought Felicity, and that's why he's
come to my table. The sun was glinting on the
knives and forks, making the jug of orange juice
sparkle, and suddenly, for no apparent reason, she
felt extraordinarily happy. She felt confident that in
spite of all her qualms she could make this tour a
success. If only she had another driver . . . anyone
but Trent. But she was stuck with him now and she
must make the best of it and ignore the fact that he regarded everything to do with the tour as a huge joke.

The passengers were all assembled in good time,
except Crystal and Denise, of course, who arrived at
the last moment, Denise yawning hugely, although
it was past ten o'clock by the time they were all met
together. Crystal had changed into what she evidently thought were more suitable clothes—a cream
slacks suit, very beautifully tailored, light beige
sandals and a polo-necked sweater in a lovely shade
of purple that exactly matched those violet eyes.
Denise on the other hand wore denim jeans with the
Gucci label and a baggy sweater of light blue. They
had changed over from one front seat to the other,
and Felicity noted that they were nearer to Trent
that way. Who had given up their seats this time?
Anne and Edith? Felicity saw that the two Australian
women had installed themselves in a back seat.

'We prefer this,' they assured her when she went to
protest about their being edged out of the good front

seats. 'Don't worry, no one can push us around unless we want it. Let Madame have her seat. Much more peaceful for you, and no one else minds. If they did, they'd say so.'

It was foolish to feel nettled because Crystal had got her own way so easily. As Edith had said, none of the other passengers objected, and the scenery was very plainly visible from all the wide windows of the coach. They were passing along a highway now, having left beautiful Victoria behind. It was close to Georgia Strait and the sunlight glittered on the wide stretch of water and the long golden beaches with lonely fishermen casting their lines into the sunlit waves. Through the Cowichan River Valley they drove and on to Nanaimo with its old wooden houses.

'This was Indian country,' Felicity told her passengers. 'The name Nanaimo comes from an Indian word meaning "where the big tribe dwells". It must have been an utterly wonderful place for the Indians to live in before the white man came. They had all this superb part of Canada for their own. They didn't have to learn how to cultivate crops, as there was game and fish and enough natural herbs and berries to provide food in plenty.'

'And now it's called the Hub and Tub town,' Trent said unexpectedly. 'Hub because it's the centre for commerce around here and the place where you catch the mainland ferries, tub because every year there's a race for bathtubs powered with outboard engines to get across from Nanaimo to Vancouver.'

'I guess that's more fun than swotting up the history of Indians,' said Denise. 'Why didn't we come when something exciting like that was going on?'

'It looks pretty good to me right now,' said Olaf, coming to the rescue.

They had descended from the coach to stretch

their legs and, over the bay, a shining white ferry-
boat was heading for the land. The white sails of
yachts were like swans upon the water, and small
fishing boats were setting out on their expeditions.
All over the bay great rafts of logs were building up,
a sign that they were in the centre of the timber
industry. Olaf stood beside Felicity pointing out
different points of interest, but she noticed that
Crystal and Denise had engaged Trent in animated
conversation. She wondered whether they had
realised when they dined with him last night that he
was not the usual kind of coach driver. He had too
great an air of assurance to deceive anyone for very
long.

And now, driving north from Nanaimo, the road
had beach on one side, forest on the other. Tiny
seaside cottages hid among trees almost on the edge
of the water, and holidaymakers wandered over the
long sands, collecting shells, digging for clams or
simply amusing themselves in whatever way they
thought best. Then the coach made a detour into
forest land with dark cedars and the lighter hemlock,
firs and alders making a tapestry of green upon the
slopes.

Their object was to be a place where they could
see a most beautiful waterfall, rushing in rapids,
swifter and swifter down the river, tumbling over
rocks and boulders until dramatically it fell in a narrow chasm to join the river in foaming splendour
hundreds of feet below. The coach had parked some
distance away and the passengers followed the forest
trail beside flowering lupins and white daisies in the
grass through towering trees smelling deliciously of
greenery.

'Isn't it great to be out of that stuffy old coach!'
exclaimed Denise. 'Come on, Al, last one there's a
dope!'

She seized hold of his hand and Al, with a rather sheepish look at Mary Lou, raced off down the pathway with her.

'Why don't you go too?' asked Edith.

'Why should I?' asked Mary Lou. 'I couldn't care less who gets there first.'

She walked slowly along with Edith and Anne, looking, Felicity thought, distinctly put out. Crystal meanwhile had lingered behind and joined Trent who was bringing up the rear. She could hear that low, sexy voice sounding very persuasive.

'I'm sure you don't really want to see those falls, Trent. In your job you must have seen them hundreds of times. You don't always have to support your courier, do you? How say we sit on that log over there? We can wait until the others come back. I don't go for using up too much energy on useless pastimes, do you?'

She could not hear Trent's murmured reply, but it brought a responsive laugh from Crystal. She glanced behind and saw Crystal touch him lightly on the face.

'Aren't you the wicked one? Do let's sit for a while.'

The hand that had been touching his cheek now slid to his palm and she saw them wandering off to a fallen tree well out of the way of the path. Why should she feel so irritated with Trent and Crystal? Felicity wondered. It was much better that Crystal seemed to have diverted Trent's attention from herself. If he was interested in Crystal then she need not be on her guard against him for the rest of the trip, and that was all to the good, wasn't it?

At the falls, the passengers spread themselves around, using their cameras, exclaiming over the strength of the cataract as it poured tumultuously over the brink. Below, great logs had wedged themselves in the rocks where the foaming water fed a narrow gorge. Denise was clambering over boulders above the rapids, encouraging Al to wilder and wilder daring.

'She really shouldn't be doing that,' said Felicity worriedly to Olaf, who had joined her. Denise had reached a rock that was high over the place where the water suddenly took its downward course.

'Denise,' she shouted, 'come back!' but either the girl chose to take no notice or the noise of the water drowned Felicity's voice.

Olaf cupped his hands and shouted with a voice that reverberated over the water and the rocks.

'Denise, come back! You are in danger there.'

Denise looked up and suddenly she appeared to realise in what peril she had placed herself. She seemed to freeze.

'I can't!' she shouted. Her voice seemed to trail into a terrified whimper. 'I daren't walk back.'

'You get her, Al,' Felicity cried.

He was standing on a safer rock not very far from Denise, and they could see him speaking to her.

'I can't get her to come,' he yelled. 'The little fool won't budge.'

'Don't worry, I'll go,' Olaf told Felicity.

By this time the other passengers had gathered together full of concern, but there was no sign of Trent and Crystal. Just as well, thought Felicity. Crystal's hysterics at this moment would be the very end. She watched as Olaf spoke gently and persuasively to the terrified girl, and saw him edge himself carefully over the slippery rocks to where Denise stood frozen with fear above the foaming gorge of the river.

Felicity closed her eyes as she saw him persuading Denise to take the step from one rock to the other. There was no sound, only the water's roar and the

sighing of wind in the high trees, and then a gasp
from the spectators . . . was it dismay? No, simply
relief. They were back again on the bank and Denise
was weeping hysterically. She began to run along the
path back to the coach and Felicity ran after her.
Crystal was still sitting with Trent on the log, but
at the sight of Denise, she jumped up hurriedly and
demanded, 'What on earth has been going on?'

'Oh, it was so frightening! I almost fell,' sobbed
Denise. 'I couldn't get back. I thought I was going
to go over the edge of the falls. The noise of the water
was terrifying!'

Crystal clasped the weeping girl in her arms and
glared at Felicity.

'Miss Tait, are you or are you not paid to look
after your passengers? How could you have let her get
into such danger? She might easily have been killed!'

'I quite agree. She gave us all a dreadful fright.'
Edith had joined them. 'She's old enough to have
more sense. You can't expect Felicity to play nursemaid to a seventeen-year-old girl.'

'Nobody asked you for your opinion, Miss Bowden. I hold Miss Tait responsible for anything that
happens on this tour, and leading my daughter into
danger is irresponsible, to say the least.'

'It's your daughter who's the irresponsible one,'
Anne now accused her.

'Please leave it,' Felicity implored the two
Australians. 'We're all shaken and liable to say
things we don't mean in the heat of the moment.'

So far she had not looked at Trent, but now she
stole a glance in his direction. What was he thinking?
It was hard to tell. His expression as he looked at her
was cool. Could he really think she had been at fault?
Crystal turned to him and said, 'Oh, Trent, if you'd
been there this would never have happened. Thank
goodness there's someone with some sense of res-

ponsibility on this tour!'

'And if Olaf hadn't been there you might have lost your daughter,' said Anne indignantly. 'He took a great risk, and so far no one has even thanked him.'

'It was nothing,' said Olaf modestly.

'Did you get her back? Well, thank you, Mr. Gustaffsen, but someone should have watched that Denise didn't get into danger in the first place,' snapped Crystal.

The passengers were a little subdued after this, and Felicity herself felt rather low. She looked unseeingly at the lovely long beaches and the stretch of sea that widened eventually into farmlands as they came nearer to Courtenay. The snowcapped mountains were still distant here. There was still most of the tour to cover. How was it going to go if she had trouble like this right from the outset? She thought hopefully of the supply of cheese and wine and savoury biscuits and cocktail goodies that she had stored in the refrigerator compartment of the coach, for she had planned a get-together of all the passengers when they arrived at Courtenay. There was nothing like a cheese and wine party to loosen tongues and make people friendly and easy with each other.

But at first it seemed otherwise. She had taken great trouble to arrange her party in a glassed-in conservatory that was cool and pretty with indoor plants. The cheeses looked appetising with the array of varied biscuits, olives, nuts, savoury titbits on sticks, the light wine glinted rosily in the glasses, but the tourists were stiff, sitting on chairs sedately ranged against the wall. Al and Mary Lou were the only ones who seemed to be speaking, and perhaps it would have been better if they were not.

'If you start running after her again this evening, I warn you I'm quitting this tour,' she heard Mary Lou say in a harsh, low voice.

'Oh, stow it, can't you!' Al whispered furiously.
'Can't I even look at another chick without your
creating a scene?'

Edith and Anne Bowden came to Felicity's rescue
as regards the party, chatting easily to the others,
getting people into groups, and Olaf too was a great
help, handing round the plates, seeing that everyone
was served with drinks. Trent was still nowhere to be
seen, although Felicity had mentioned the party to
him and would normally have expected any other
driver to help her. But he was a law to himself. Nor
were Crystal and Denise here. The party was well
under way, a buzz of conversation and laughter
taking the place of the rather deadly shyness there
had been at first, when at last Denise came in. She
had not bothered to change from her jeans, although
now she wore a tubular arrangement that exposed
her young lovely shoulders. Helping herself to a
Coke, she made a beeline for Al. Mary Lou turned
her back and went over to Olaf, engaging him in
animated conversation. This was a pity, as he had
been so helpful in getting people together and now he
couldn't get away from Mary Lou.

Now in came Crystal with Trent. She was dressed
far too elaborately for the occasion in a short tight
sparkling dress with shoestring straps, high-heeled
silver slippers to match, and she was carrying a
silver fox fur wrap. Her black shining hair was coiled
up in an intricate knot on one side of her head and in
her ears were long diamond ear-rings. As she made her
entrance, she turned to Trent, who was following close
behind her, and put one hand possessively on his arm.

'We thought we must have just one drink at your
party, Felicity,' she said. 'Trent and I are going out
to dinner. He says he knows of a little place where we
can get French food. I must say he's wonderfully
well informed, your coach driver. Where does the

company find such men?'

No romantic complications, thought Felicity.
That seemed to be the company's strict rule. But
what would a rule matter to Trent? He was too
accustomed to being a law to himself. Good heavens,
Felicity, she told herself, you should be exceedingly
thankful that Crystal seems to have diverted Trent's
interest from yourself. So why feel this wave of irritation at seeing these two together? Beautiful people
—that exactly describes them. So good-looking, so
sure of themselves. They both inhabit the same world,
it's obvious. But why did I have to be burdened with
them on this, my first and so important trip?

She moved around, chatting to her guests, giving
them information about the forthcoming journey,
trying to get to know them better. Except for Crystal
and Denise, and, of course, Trent, she had been
remarkably fortunate in the people who had joined
the tour. There was quite a mixture, Canadians,
Hollanders, Australians, but they all seemed to be
getting on together well. However, Denise was still
fascinating Al, it seemed, and Mary Lou had moved
over to talk to the Australians. This left Olaf free,
and he made a beeline for Felicity. She was glad to
talk to him, because it took her mind off the sight of
Crystal, hand on Trent's arm, violet eyes gazing
expressively up at him. Yes, he seemed to be finding
her very fascinating, and she seemed to be the kind
of woman who might appeal to his footloose philosophy, the kind who would enjoy giving it a whirl
with a handsome man, enjoying a brief holiday
romance. But that's not for me, thought Felicity.
Trent made a great mistake in thinking so.

Now she saw Crystal gathering up her fox wrap
and going over for a word with Denise. At the same
time she realised that Trent was moving over in her
direction. He was standing beside her now and she

was conscious of his gold-green eyes regarding her
and Olaf with a sparkle of mocking humour. Olaf
moved away presumably because he thought Trent
and she had some private business to discuss. For the
party Felicity had changed into a light cotton dress
in a delicate shade of green with sprigs of pink and
blue flowers. It had a full skirt with a deep frill and
a drawstring neck, a complete change from the
severity of her daytime uniform. She had brushed
her hair down in waves upon her shoulders. Now,
compared with Crystal's elegant sophistication, she
felt rather countrified and too young-looking.

Trent put out his hand and touched the red-gold
waves of her hair, seemingly regardless of the
interested glances in their direction. She drew away
abruptly, alarmed by the sudden thrill that coursed
through her body like a surge of electricity. How
well he knows the charm of that smile, she thought,
even when he's making fun of me.

'I like it,' he told her. 'If you were my . . . shall we
say, wife . . . you'd always wear your hair like this. I
would demand it.'

'Do you always expect to get what you demand?'
she couldn't help asking.

'Naturally, and if I were so foolish as to ever take a
wife, I would expect one who would treat my smal-
lest demand as law.'

'Poor creature! Even if you asked her to shave her
head?'

'Maybe. But you need never be afraid I'll demand
that of you, Felicity.'

'I should hope not! But I thought you were
against such luxuries as wives.'

'I am indeed. What started this conversation,
anyhow? I came to ask if you propose to make an
early start?'

'Yes, I do. We have to get the ferry at Beaver Cove

near Port Hardy by mid-afternoon and the country around the Campbell River is worth seeing. I don't want to have to rush it.'

'Right, I'll see to that. Any chance of a nightcap if I come to discuss tomorrow's arrangements in more detail when I return?'

'I hardly think that will be necessary. I'll give you all instructions tomorrow.'

Crystal wafted over to them, bringing with her a heady gust of French perfume.

'Denise has her own ideas about what she's going to do this evening,' she said. 'Felicity, would you be a dear and check that she's in her room by midnight? I've told her you'll do that. Otherwise she'll be in the disco with her new friend until all hours and I don't want her to stay up late. If she isn't in her room, you could wrinkle her out from the disco. O.K.?'

Without waiting for an answer, she took Trent's arm and waved a cheerful goodbye to the assembled guests.

So now Felicity was expected to play nursemaid to Denise, a task she hardly relished. But what was happening between Al and Mary Lou? They had seemed such a couple of lovebirds when the tour began, and now Denise seemed to be changing all that. Gradually the party broke up after Trent and Crystal had departed. Edith, Anne and Olaf stayed behind to help clear.

'There's such a lot of cheese and salami and stuff left over here,' said Anne. 'Couldn't we take it to make a picnic tomorrow?'

'Certainly,' said Felicity. 'We go through Campbell River country on our way to Port Hardy where we get the ferry. I've got flasks in the coach and we can make coffee and buy fruit.'

'Coffee would be good right now,' Olaf suggested. 'How about a stroll down the main street in search of some?'

But Edith and Anne declared they had to catch up with correspondence. Olaf looked rather downcast, Felicity thought, so she said, 'Give me an hour to clear my arrangements and then I'll come for a walk with you. I would like it.'

She had engaged a kind of bedsitting room for herself with a desk where she could go over her papers. She had not been sitting here long, however, when there was a tentative knock on the door. 'Come in,' she called, and the door was pushed open by Mary Lou. Her hair was tousled as if she had been lying down and Felicity thought she looked as if she had been weeping.

'What is it, Mary Lou?' asked Felicity, but she thought she knew the answer already.

'I come to ask you how I can get home from here. I want to leave the tour.'

'Oh, but, Mary Lou, aren't you enjoying it?'

She knew this was a silly question. The girl looked so forlorn, such a contrast to the bright young thing who had chatted so happily on the first day.

'I'm sorry you want to go,' Felicity said. 'Isn't there anything I could do about it?'

'No way. I guess you know what's bugging me—Denise. She's gone for Al like a man-eating tiger ever since we joined this trip, and I just can't take it any more. I want out. I guess the only way is to quit.' And Mary Lou began to weep.

'I thought it was going to be great, coming away with Al, having this time to ourselves, away from the families, but it hasn't worked out that way.'

Felicity put her arm around the girl's shoulders.

'Please don't be so upset, Mary Lou. It's early days yet. We've hardly started. Denise is very young and just at the stage where she's determined to attract attention. Al is a bit flattered, but I'm sure he'll get over it. She doesn't really mean a thing to him. He's such a nice guy, he doesn't know how to snub her when she pays attention to him. I would just ignore it, honestly I would.'

Mary Lou's large brown eyes gazed at her trustingly.

'Do you really mean that?'

It was obvious that she very much wanted to believe Felicity.

'I'm sure of it. Don't show that it bugs you. Just take an interest in the trip. Show that you're enjoying yourself. Make yourself as agreeable as you can, and that way Al will feel that you're independent and next thing he'll come running. Want to bet?'

Mary Lou smiled through her tears.

'I don't really want to go home. I've looked forward to this trip for so long. O.K., I'll try to be pleasant, but—oh, gee, I get so mad when I see Denise rolling her eyes at him!'

'I know,' said Felicity, and, to her surprise, she had a fleeting vision of Crystal, her violet eyes concentrated on Trent—but what had that got to do with the present situation? She could not be mad at Crystal—or could she? Don't be ridiculous, Felicity told herself. Mary Lou is in love with Al. The set-up is entirely different.

'Give it a go for a little while longer, Mary Lou,' she advised. 'I'm sure you'll find you'll begin to enjoy the tour. If you go home now, you'll only spend the time pining after Al. Wouldn't you rather be on the spot where you can do something about your problem?'

'That's right,' Mary Lou admitted. 'I guess I'd better quit griping and try something more subtle. Thanks a million, Felicity—is it all right if I call you that?'

'Sure,' said Felicity, thankful that she seemed to have skirted a dangerous spot. She truly wanted

Mary Lou to be as happy as she had been when the tour started, but she must admit to herself that if one of its number had opted out it would be a black mark against her. At least she had sent Mary Lou away less miserable than when she came, and she hoped this trouble would blow over. She tried now to concentrate on her work concerning the future arrangements. She was determined that as far as was in her power everything should go well. There were one or two points on which she could have used Trent's help. He knew more about the route than she did herself, and, remembering his suggestion of a nightcap when he came in, she wondered whether she should have accepted his offer of a late-night visit. But no, she was sure he had forgotten about this already, because he was too involved with Crystal tonight.

But Olaf had not forgotten her. She had almost finished her work when there was a discreet tap on the door.

'Finished your work?'

He had come in rather eagerly as soon as she murmured a response to his knock. He really was handsome, Felicity thought, like one's idea of a Viking but not as fierce, of course—golden beard, good physique, sea blue eyes, short golden curls. Any girl would be pleased to have him for an escort. And he was so eager to please, so—well, almost deferential, far pleasanter than Trent with whom every conversation seemed to turn into a duel of wits. Yes, she would enjoy the evening with Olaf and put the thought of Trent and his present companion right out of her mind.

They strolled along the sidewalk, stopping every now and again to look at shops, some with tourist junk, some with really beautiful Indian carvings and Eskimo ones of soapstone, some with arrays of heavy

Cowichan sweaters in handknitted natural wools with designs of eagles and other symbols. In a side street Felicity noticed a small restaurant with a French name, 'La Petite Hirondelle.' They both looked in curiously, able to see over the café curtains that hung halfway up the windows with heavy wooden rings. There were small tables very dimly lit and very soft, romantic music could be heard faintly. Then Felicity flinched away from the window as if she had been stung, for she had seen Trent and Crystal sitting in a corner of the room, their faces half revealed by the golden candlelit glow, the rest of them in deep shadow. Crystal's features, normally a little hard, were softened and made lovelier by the gentle, flattering illumination, and Trent's dark, handsome face looked somehow glamorous like a painting of a hero of long ago.

'Would you like to have coffee and dessert here?' asked Olaf. 'I should think that's all we could manage after your so excellent party.'

'Oh, no,' said Felicity. 'Let's find another place, please.'

'Certainly. I go for your ice cream parlours. How about one of those?'

Sitting in the noisy ice cream parlour at a shining white table under glittering lights and assailed by the constant din from a jukebox nearby, Felicity ate her maple nut sundae and tried not to think of Trent and Crystal in the little French bistro with the intimate atmosphere that must lead to whispered confidences and heighten whatever feeling of romance existed between them. Don't be stupid, Felicity, she told herself. If you've wanted to dine with Trent, you could have done that very first evening before Crystal took over. You're much more comfortable with Olaf, and safer too.

'This place is rather amusing and very lively,

don't you find it so?' asked Olaf.

He was watching the varied crowd, the young people in T-shirts and jeans playing the fruit machines, the families sitting at the tables with young children busily scooping up their dishes of ice cream.

'When I see young girls, I'm reminded of my own daughter,' he said.

'You have a daughter?' asked Felicity, surprised, because somehow she had got the impression of Olaf as a loner.

'My wife died about five years ago. My daughter lives with her grandparents. I would like to make a home for her, but it is difficult for a man alone.'

'I'm sorry,' said Felicity.

'Don't be. Time cures the hurt. I try to do some travelling each year to see a different part of the world, and this time, as soon as we met, I sensed, how would you say it, that it was going to be particularly enjoyable. It has been a great pleasure meeting someone like you, Felicity—I hope you don't mind if I call you by that name.'

'Of course not. I'm glad you're enjoying the tour, but it's hardly begun yet. There's much better to come.'

'Indeed I hope so.'

Olaf was looking at her with that rather significant expression she had noticed before. No romance, she thought to herself firmly.

'I really must get back,' she said, 'because I still have one or two things to clear up.'

'Let me help you if I can. I'll order that coffee we intended to have some hours ago.'

She found it difficult to insist that she would prefer to be alone. With quiet persistence, Olaf somehow convinced her that she needed him and coffee too, and presently they were in her bedsitting room and he was helping her tie up the ends of her arrangements for the next day. It was after midnight when he got up to leave.

'You've been very kind,' she said.

'You're welcome,' he smiled. 'Isn't that what you Canadians say?'

'I'm not truly Canadian,' she told him. 'I was brought up in England.'

'Ah, so. That accounts for that rather reserved manner.'

'I don't think I'm reserved,' Felicity protested. 'It wouldn't be appropriate to be reserved in a job like mine.'

'Perhaps not, but there's just that rather charming manner, a sense of—what is it?—perhaps shyness, that acts as a kind of challenge. You are very lovely, Felicity, too lovely to be alone with.'

To her surprise, for she had thought him completely trustworthy, he caught her in a strong embrace and bent his head to kiss her. His beard was like rippled silk against her skin and she felt totally embarrassed by this unexpected turn of events. She thought it would be undignified, even unkind, to struggle with this man, and yet it was like being embraced by some muscular bear. 'No, Olaf, please!' she managed to gasp out, but he did not seem to hear, and then suddenly the door burst open and Trent stood on the threshold.

Had he knocked? If he had, Felicity had not heard it. Olaf immediately dropped his arms to his sides and stood there frowning and looking disconcerted. As well he might, thought Felicity, confronted by that expression on Trent's face. He seemed furiously angry, his tanned face flushed, the dark brows frowning. And what had he to be angry about? thought Felicity. It was her affair, not Trent's, if Olaf chose to kiss her. All the same, she had been glad of the interruption.

'I came to discuss the route for tomorrow,' said Trent. 'It seems I chose a bad moment.'

'Rather call it a very beautiful moment,' Olaf said graciously. 'I'll leave you now, Felicity. Thanks for a lovely evening.'

Without looking at Trent, he went out and closed the door quietly. Felicity, feeling distinctly ruffled, smoothed down her dress and put her hands to her hair. All the time, she felt the sardonic stare of those gold-green eyes upon her.

'A very beautiful moment,' said Trent. 'Did you find it so, Felicity? Did I interrupt something important?'

'Oh, what does it matter what it was?' said Felicity crossly. 'You interrupted it anyway. That's all there is to it.'

'I rather thought the firm discouraged any suggestion of romance with the passengers.'

'So they do. But I haven't noticed that you're affected by that.'

'Now, now, your eyes are a delicious dark blue. I haven't noticed any shade of green in them,' he jeered.

'You're being quite ridiculous. How could I feel jealous of any way you choose to conduct yourself?'

'I can dream, can't I?'

How exasperating he was! she thought.

'It's impossible to be serious with you,' she said crossly. 'The whole episode is a tremendous joke to you, but I wish you could remember that the tour is very important to me. I daren't let anything go wrong.'

'So. Then let's get down to business. What help can I give you for the arrangements tomorrow?'

'Olaf has been checking for me, since you weren't here.'

'Good for Olaf! Quite the Boy Scout, isn't he? And he seemed to be getting his reward in no uncertain terms.'

'Please leave Olaf alone. He's an extremely nice man. I didn't quite expect what happened, but anyone can get carried away sometimes.'

'So they can, even my ice-cool Felicity, or was I dreaming that night when we first met?'

'I think we should both forget that evening in your house. I can promise you the situation won't arise again.'

'Ah, but I can't promise you. Look at us now. You, looking extremely charming, in that very feminine dress and your hair loose as I like it. It's after midnight and the whole hotel is quiet and asleep, or almost so. Isn't this the opportunity we've both longed for?'

He took a step towards her and she felt that frisson of fear that she had felt before when alone with him, even though she believed in her heart that he was treating this whole thing as a joke.

'I can assure you I haven't "longed for" any opportunity. All my desire is to be rid of you and have a regular driver.'

'Don't look so alarmed,' he told her. 'I've told you before, I've never made love to an unwilling woman, but, my dear Felicity, I can't believe your reactions are as cold as you would have me believe.'

He took both her hands in his and yet made no attempt to embrace her. How different this was from Olaf's bearlike hug. How was it that this man, whom she did not even like, could set up such an alarming thrill by the mere touch of his hands? He was smiling, and yet there was something serious in his expression, something mysterious and exciting behind the intense gaze of those dark green eyes flecked with tiny sparkles of gold and surrounded by a thick shield of curling black lashes.

His hands slid along the silky texture of her arms and grasped her elbows, drawing her nearer to him, and now his face was against her hair, his mouth finding the sensitive place behind her ear, causing her to feel tremulously vulnerable, though his touch was gentle as a dove's feathers and he had not even kissed her mouth. And then there was a peremptory tap upon the door.

'Damnation!' Trent growled. 'If this is Olaf . . .'

But it was Crystal, in an elegant long gown of midnight blue satin edged with lace.

'Ah, there you are. I met Olaf and he said you were here, Trent. You said of course you had to see Miss Tait when I went in search of Denise, but I expected you back. I thought we were going to have a nightcap together in my room. You and Miss Tait must have had more business to discuss than you expected.'

She looked suspiciously from one to the other. Felicity, already feeling dishevelled, felt even more so in contrast with Crystal's very soignée appearance.

'And, Miss Tait, I thought I asked you to check whether Denise was in her room,' she added. 'She was nowhere to be found when I went there, but Olaf brought her up from the discotheque, otherwise she would have been there all night. And she was with strangers. It seems Al took his girl-friend elsewhere. It really is very annoying that I've had all this trouble. If you'd done as I asked, I wouldn't have had to row with her. You seem to me to act most irresponsibly towards your guests. Are you in charge of us or not?'

Trent put one arm around the angry woman and at once she seemed to recollect herself and calm down.

'Come, let's go. What about that nightcap you promised me? Felicity has been very busy this even-

ing, what with one thing and another, and I expect
she thought Denise old enough to look after herself.'

Or Crystal old enough to look after Denise, thought
Felicity wryly as at last she got ready for bed. She did
not know with whom she felt most angry—Crystal,
Trent or maybe herself.

CHAPTER SIX

AT last, thought Felicity, the tour seemed to be
getting off its feet. Last night's party had successfully broken the ice and there was much chatter on
the coach as they headed down the coastal highway.
Yet she could not lift her own feelings of apprehension about what was to happen in the following days.

All day they would travel mainly beside the shore
where holiday cottages were built right on the
water's edge among the trees and the hazy blue
waters stretched on to the horizon and snowcapped
mountains could be seen miles away upon the mainland. The forest was still there on the other side of
the highway, with small wooden houses in the clearings and happy horses in the pastures, but now the
type of trees seemed to have changed.

'You get warmer weather here because of the
Pacific Japanese current, so this is a rain area,' Trent
told the passengers. 'The dark patches on the slopes
are cedars, and the hemlock, spruce and fir are the
lighter trees.'

'How do you know all these things?' one of the
Australians asked him.

'Because I've worked in a logging camp, among
other things. It's pretty tough, I can tell you, logging in wintertime, and tree planting too is something

else again. You have to strap two huge sacks of young trees around your waist and climb up steep slopes with a dibble to make places for them. It's very rough terrain and pretty damn freezing when you're up there. The young plants are given an artificial winter to start them off, just to put them in the right mood, I guess. They're frozen first and then sprayed with fungicides.'

'You're so rugged, Trent,' purred Crystal from her front seat, 'and yet so sophisticated. How do you manage it?'

'Years of experience,' said Trent.

There was that infuriating smile on his face. Felicity, who was sitting up front beside him, felt a great desire to wipe that smile from his face.

'Quite one of nature's gentlemen,' she observed.

'Yes, indeed,' said Trent, and, in a whispered aside that no one else could hear, 'I trust you appreciate how gentlemanly my behaviour has been towards you.'

'I don't,' Felicity told him. 'I'd appreciate it more if you would stick solely to business in our association, which, you must admit, you forced on me.'

'But nothing else has been forced, has it? Consider, Felicity, the days are rushing by and you're wasting your time with the worthy Olaf instead of finding out how wonderful this tour could be for both of us.'

'Thank you, but I have no wish to find out. And what about Crystal? Are you wasting your time with her?'

Again that infuriating smile.

'Not exactly. Crystal is a beautiful, elegant woman. Back home it's always useful to be seen around with someone like her. Adds to one's ego.'

'I'd hardly say your ego needs any additions,' said Felicity.

'You'd be surprised. I remember distinctly the first time I escorted a beautiful woman to an exclusive restaurant. It was like the first time I bought myself a gold watch.'

'And just as expensive, I expect,' said Felicity.

As they ran easily along the lovely coastline, the misty blue of the waters took on a dreamlike quality and the wooden houses among the tall trees seemed somehow unreal. What am I doing here? she thought. This tour that I thought was going to be so wonderful has turned almost into some kind of nightmare, with two women who make trouble for me all the time and a man who wants me as some kind of conquest, a scalp to hang on his belt. She shuddered, although the sunshine was pouring into the coach.

'What's wrong?' asked Trent. Without taking his eyes from the road, he put one large hand on hers. 'Goose ran over your grave?'

Felicity laughed shakily. 'Wherever did you pick that up? Our old servant used to say it.'

'God knows. Are you cold? I can turn up the heat in the coach if you like.'

'No, don't do that.'

His hand on hers meant nothing to him, she thought. It took much more than that to excite him. Why, therefore, had she felt the same dangerous thrill that she had to try furiously to disguise at the mere touch of his fingers on her own? I don't even like him, she thought. He's caused me nothing but trouble.

Approaching the town of Campbell River. Felicity tried to throw away her gloomy thoughts and concentrate on her passengers.

'This marks the boundary of the northern third of the island,' she told them. 'It was very wild to begin with and still is inland. For ages there was no road beyond Kelsey Bay, but now the highway heads across country to join up with the north island road at Woss Camp. We'll be following the road inland after Kelsey Bay, but then we come shorewards again at Port McNeill and on to Port Hardy where we get the ferry.'

They passed across the bridge over the wide mouth of the Campbell River. There were big sawmills on the coast. This part was obviously the hub of the timber industry.

'Its biggest claim to fame, however, is its salmon fishing,' said Trent. 'It's the capital of the world for that. You need to come here in May and June. The place swarms with visitors, every type of person, ordinary people, film stars, wealthy business men, all keen to catch salmon.'

'Have you been here, then?' asked Felicity.

'Naturally,' said Trent. 'I'm keen for new experiences. I think you are too, Felicity.'

'Some experiences. Not all,' she said reservedly.

'There speaks my cautious Felicity! One day I'll make you admit you desire all the experiences that I want too.'

The road led inland for some way through higher country that looked more unlived-in, more like a wilderness area, than they had seen previously, and again they emerged on the coast at Port Macneill.

'There's a tiny ferry goes to Alert Bay,' Trent told them. 'Once a year the Indians hold a salmon barbecue there and have a parade of boats, but unfortunately we're just too late for that.'

'Nothing exciting seems to be happening at the right time, does it?' said Denise. 'In fact it's all totally boring.'

Felicity had seen with relief that Mary Lou and Al seemed to be on better terms again. Mary Lou must have taken her advice and made it up with Al, or perhaps Al had repented of his interest in Denise. This must have left Denise out in the cold, for she was looking very sulky and ill-tempered, hardly even saying a word to Crystal and gazing with blank boredom out of the windows of the coach, her mouth in constant motion as she chewed gum.

In mid-afternoon they came to Bear Cove where they were to pick up the ferry that would take them right up the Inner Passage to Prince Rupert, the farthest north they were to go. For Felicity it would be a period of rest from the togetherness of the coach journey, for they would be on the boat overnight and during this time she hoped the passengers would be prepared to look after themselves. Maybe she could get a rest from Trent too. Crystal would probably be only too ready to take him off her hands.

She felt a lift of her heart as she saw the ferryboat coming into land. Temporarily her depression seemed to vanish as she saw the neat white vessel upon which they were to spend the night, because it looked so attractive. The afternoon light was brilliant, the boat standing out clearcut upon the blue waters of the bay with the paler blue sky behind and the sun flashing fire upon every bit of polished metal.

The coach was in a queue of vehicles and Felicity found that Trent was standing beside her watching the boat edging its way in. For once she felt glad of his company.

'It's silly, isn't it, but I can never help feeling excited about a journey upon water, however short it may be,' she said.

'Yes, there's something about a sea voyage that's romantic even today,' he agreed. 'But wait until you see my yacht. That's the way to travel if you want an exhilarating time.'

'I guess it might be too exhilarating,' said Felicity.

I'll never see your yacht, she wanted to say. What nonsense you talk!

'You must learn to like excitement. I thrive on it.'

Of course you would, she thought.

While the passengers waited around for the signal to drive on to the ferry, Felicity noticed that Al and Mary Lou seemed to be on good terms again. Denise had wandered off far from the main party and was talking in animated fashion to some young men and girls on motorbikes. They were clad in tight black leather jeans and jackets and carried highly coloured safety helmets. Crystal had stayed in the coach, doing some complicated repairs to her face.

At last the gates were raised and the coaches and cars were allowed into the great gaping maw of the ferry.

'Take everything you require for overnight with you,' Felicity advised her passengers. 'We won't be able to come down here again until tomorrow morning.'

Amidst the hustle of passengers coming and going and all the noise connected with a boat getting ready for departure, Felicity conferred with a steward to place her passengers in the cabins allotted to them. When she had successfully disposed of them all, she said, 'I almost forgot to ask you for the number of my own cabin.'

'Oh, yes, let's see. You're sharing a cabin with someone called Seymour.'

'But . . . but . . .' Felicity stammered, 'are you sure? What's the initial?'

'T.—a Mrs T. Seymour.'

'There isn't any Mrs T. Seymour. That's my driver, Trent Seymour, and I'm certainly not willing to share a cabin with him!'

'Your driver? There must have been a box-up. Ah, yes, I see it's not "Mrs" but "Mr T. Seymour" and they have you down as "Mr F. Tait." It seems they thought you were both men. They often have a male courier on this run.'

'Well, they haven't this time. I hope you have another cabin vacant for Mr Seymour. The tour's pretty strenuous and we both need our rest.'

The steward ran his pencil down the list, looking harassed.

'I'm afraid not. The boat's completely full for this run.'

'What about Olaf Gustaffsen? Hasn't he got a cabin Mr Seymour could share?'

'No, he's sharing with a Mr Al Draper. I'm so sorry, Miss Tait, I'll see what I can do later on for you. Someone may have cancelled or not have turned up.'

He hurried off to where other people were waiting to question him. Suddenly there was Trent standing behind her.

'What's the trouble?' he asked. 'You look ruffled.'

'They thought I was a man and have put us together in the same cabin,' Felicity explained.

He threw back his head and the bronzed column of his throat vibrated.

'Stop laughing! It isn't funny. We both need to have a proper sleep tonight and now one of us will have to sleep on deck, and it won't be me!'

In spite of her annoyance at the situation, his laughter was infectious.

'That's better. Smile, Felicity. Don't look so fussed—it's not the end of the world. If you won't have me in your cabin—and, by your reaction, it's evident you think you'd face a fate worse than death by letting me sleep there—I'll snatch some sleep on one of the reclining chairs if they aren't claimed by the time I get there.'

He made her feel foolish and puritanical, but she was determined she could not share the same sleeping quarters with him. Was she afraid of him? Yes, partly that. But even more so she was afraid of herself. She had never before met a man to whom her physical self reacted so strongly, and she didn't trust this reaction.

'Well now,' suggested Trent, 'let's find this famous cabin and dispose of our belongings. At least you won't mind my leaving my overnight bag there, will you?'.

'No, of course not.'

He put his arm around her shoulders and guided her down the brightly lit passage to the cabin that had been allotted to them.

'It's very tiny, isn't it?' said Felicity.

There were two bunks, one on top of the other, and a very small washroom.

'What does it matter? It's only intended for overnight travel,' said Trent.

In the tiny space he was so close to her that she could smell the scent of his aftershave lotion, something that reminded her of green forests and waterfalls, very simple and probably frightfully expensive. He was wearing a safari jacket and as he leaned over to place his overnight bag on the rack above the bunk, he brushed against her and she felt the silky hair of his arm against her cheek. She flinched away from this intimate sensation and was conscious that his eyes were upon her, as if he were analysing her reaction and drawing some conclusion of his own.

'Look, Felicity, there's no need to leap like a startled deer when I touch you. I get the message. There's not going to be any big seduction scene here and now. I reckon we need a more romantic setting than this rabbit hutch.'

'There's not going to be any setting at all, Trent,' said Felicity.

She wished she could stop this stupid trembling. He was so close to her that she was sure he must be aware of it. Pull yourself together, Felicity, she told

herself. He's not the first man in the world to want
to make love to you. And you dealt quite efficiently
with the others. But you yourself didn't have the
same reaction, she reminded herself, and that shows
you have to be infinitely more careful.

'Let's forget our problems about sleeping accom-
modation for the time being, shall we?' said Trent.
'There's still hours of daylight left, so you can enjoy
the thrill of a sea voyage up on deck. You told me you
found it romantic.'

'It was you who said it was romantic,' she reminded
him.

'So I did. Well, we deserve a few hours' vacation
on this boat. Let's forget the passengers and enjoy
the voyage.'

Had he forgotten about Crystal already? Surely
not. He seemed to be concentrating on being charming to Felicity herself now, or was this a kind of
opportunism? she wondered. Because of the mix-up
about the cabin, had he decided this was a good
chance to further the plans he had announced at the
beginning of the tour? Whatever his ideas, Felicity
knew that she did not trust him.

As they emerged from the tiny cabin, she was
surprised to see Denise only a few yards down the
narrow passageway. She stared at them, her eyes
wide and surprised-looking with their doll-like
lashes. Her mass of blonde hair was loose and frizzed
out from a centre parting so that she looked like some
old painting of an angel, and yet the hard expression
of her eyes was anything but angelic. She was wearing the inevitable jeans and a skimpy tube that showed her shining, bronzed shoulders.

'Oh, Miss Tait, Crystal sent me to see you.'
Felicity had noticed before that Denise called her
mother by her Christian name. 'She's left some make-
up in the coach and she wants Trent to get it for her.

She can't do without it. And we've been given a crazy sort of stateroom that's only fit for midgets. She wants you to see the purser and get it changed.'

'I doubt very much whether anything can be done about it, Denise. Most of them are this size and there are no spare staterooms available.'

'But do we have to share? Couldn't I get one of my own?'

'I'm sorry, there just isn't one vacant,' said Felicity.

'I guess you have a cabin to yourself,' sniffed Denise.

She looked enquiringly with those fallen angel eyes at Trent. Trent shrugged.

'Not exactly,' he said. 'I'll go see about unlocking the coach. I'll see you later, Felicity.' And off he went.

'How about Al?' Denise persisted. 'Is he sharing a cabin with his darling Mary Lou?'

'No, of course not. Mary Lou is sharing with one of the ladies from Holland and Al is sharing with Olaf.'

'A pity,' said Denise. 'I wouldn't mind shacking up with him.'

'You don't need to try to shock me, Denise. It's not clever.'

A spark of anger flared in those huge brown eyes.

'And it's not clever to interfere in places where you aren't wanted. I'd almost begun to enjoy this trip. Al isn't exactly a number one heart-throb, but he was good fun until you told Mary Lou she should stop being mad and make up to him again. Now he's gone back to her and doesn't want to know my troubles. And I'm bored, bored, bored!'

Denise kicked her scarlet sandal against the wood-work of the doorway, and then suddenly seemed transfixed by something she saw there. Felicity saw that she was reading the slip of paper in the holder on the door and realised that her own and Trent's names were typed there.

Denise turned around angrily to Felicity.

'I see you have your own fun organised, even if you do interfere with mine. We thought all along that you weren't as goody-goody as you made out. Just wait until I tell Crystal! Is she ever going to be wild!'

And before Felicity could say a word, she had dashed down the passageway like a particularly agile young wildcat.

Feeling nettled, Felicity went inside the cabin again. I'm determined to enjoy this voyage, she thought, in spite of everything. She changed from the uniform she had still been wearing into a pair of sky blue slacks with a blue and white striped top, low cut with narrow straps. Over this she wore a fluffy blue sweater, but she hoped it would be warm enough on deck to discard it. On her feet she put red espadrilles which laced up her leg and had rope soles to make her surefooted on deck, and she knotted a red spotted kerchief around her neck. The effect was rather dashing, she thought, as she looked at herself in the tiny mirror.

Ascending the stairway, she found herself on the promenade deck. Although by now it was late afternoon, the sun was still quite high and shining brilliantly upon the glittering blue water. All parts of the boat were shining white, including the seats with comfortable, curving backs that were placed for viewing where the foaming wake traced the passage of the boat over the sheltered waterway. Felicity sat down upon the farthermost seat she could find and watched in delight as the scenery unfolded before her, so many small islands blanketed with trees and with snow-covered mountains towering up in the distance. Trees, trees, trees, right down to the water's edge— coastal rain forest, she thought, remembering some of her reading about the tour. They passed little fishing boats trolling upon the smooth water and she thought how strange and wild the life of the fishermen must be compared with that in the big cities.

It was very peaceful sitting here, feeling the boat throbbing under her feet, hearing the swish of the water and the call of a seabird hovering over the wake. A skein of wild geese passed overhead, their honking cries coming clear over the sounds of the passengers' chatter. Some of the people from the coach were sitting quite near to her, but so interested were they in the passing scenery that they left her alone, not even plying her with questions as was their usual custom.

But her peace was not to last for long. Something deep inside her gave a nervous throb as she heard Trent's voice, the deep, laughing enthusiasm of his tone, followed by Crystal's smooth Boston accent. They were coming towards her and there was no avoiding it. Crystal had changed into a chalk-white sundress with larger than lifesize red poppies appliquéd in a simple design upon the bell-like skirt. Her dark hair was swept up in a French pleat and she wore gold gypsy ear-rings. The dress displayed her beautiful tan to its utmost advantage. Trent had discarded his jacket and his blue shirt was open to the waist above the golden bronze of his chest.

'Oh, there you are, Felicity,' said Crystal in a voice that was all sweetness and light.

Felicity was surprised, for Crystal had always before spoken to her in the coolest of tones. Moreover, she had thought Crystal would be annoyed with her, first on account of her tiny cabin and second because Denise was sure to have told her that Trent had his name on hers.

'How cute you look, Felicity—quite nautical, isn't she, Trent? Those old uniforms must get pretty boring. They certainly look it. I can't think why the company doesn't provide you with something more becoming.'

Felicity, who up to this moment had thought her uniform very smart, sensed the underlying cattiness that lay in these remarks, but nevertheless it was rather wounding. How perfect Crystal looked in the low-cut dress that showed off her beautiful figure to perfection. It was hard to believe that she was the mother of Denise, who was already so adult.

'Isn't Trent the eighth wonder of the world?' Crystal went on. 'He fought the crew to open the hold and get my cosmetic bag for me. I truly couldn't have survived without it. And he's fixed it so I have a bigger stateroom. I couldn't possibly have managed in the midget size specimen they gave us at first. He seems to have more respect for his passengers' wellbeing than you have, Felicity, if you don't mind my saying so.'

But I do mind your saying so, thought Felicity. How had Trent managed this when the steward had been so adamant that there were no staterooms left? She looked at them both, Crystal with her slender red-tipped hand intimately clasping Trent's bare arm, Trent looking down at them both with a smile in his eyes, as usual very pleased with himself. What powers of persuasion had he used to make someone give up a larger stateroom? The same charm that he must use in his business relationships, she supposed, or in all his relationships, for that matter. How could one believe that he was ever sincere? In everything he did she sensed an ulterior motive.

Crystal turned to her with a honeyed smile, but her violet eyes were watchful, like those of a Siamese cat using its wiles to get an extra piece of chicken.

'And, Felicity, I have a wee favour to ask of you. I don't think you'll mind, will she, Trent? I've discussed it with him too. I'm very exhausted after all the travelling and Denise is determined to stay up late tonight. She's found a crowd of friends of her own age. We wondered if you would mind sharing your cabin with her. She won't be any trouble, I assure you. She'll creep in, quiet as a mouse, she's promised. And then I can get my rest. Unfortunately I wake so easily. I'm terribly sensitive and highly strung, so much so that I suffer most dreadfully from insomnia.'

What is this? wondered Felicity. Her mind whirled around all the possibilities. One thing was certain— Denise must have told her mother about the two names on the cabin door. Did Crystal think that by foisting Denise upon her she would spoil her own plans? And what was the real reason that Crystal wanted the stateroom to herself if it was a larger one anyway? Did she intend to entertain Trent there? Felicity suddenly felt tired of both of them. Crystal had obviously cooked this thing up with Trent's consent. Was it Trent's way of getting back at her because she had been so fussed about the mix-up with the cabin? What can it matter to me if Trent and Crystal intend to have an affair? she thought. It solves my problem about sharing the cabin anyway. She smiled to herself at the idea of Denise being a safeguard and a chaperone.

At the sight of this smile, Crystal relaxed. She had been gazing intently at Felicity with that pansy blue stare as if she were trying to hypnotise her, but now she turned and lifted those lovely eyes to Trent.

'Of course you said she wouldn't mind. You are a gem, isn't she, Trent?'

The emerald gold eyes flickered over her, and she felt foolishly aware of her bare shoulders and the heart-shaped top that revealed more than they concealed of her small, curving breasts.

'A jewel,' he said. 'And in some respects diamond-hard.'

CHAPTER SEVEN

THEY turned away, strolling along the deck, Crystal with her hand on Trent's arm. Felicity saw several people turn to look at them, for they really were a striking couple. So now she could relax as she had wished to do without any thought of the mix-up about the cabin. The whole problem had been solved, it seemed, and she had not asked Trent where he intended to spend the night because she thought she knew. Why then should this worry her? And yet she found she could not put the thought of Trent and Crystal out of her mind. She had had experience of other tours and the way, after just a few days in holiday surroundings, certain people could become drawn towards each other almost as if magnetised. I'm not the guardian of their morals, she said now firmly to herself. No way. I'm merely employed to do my side of the business, which is to see that the tour keeps running smoothly.

What had you been expecting? she asked herself. A kind of dialogue was taking place in her brain between the efficient Felicity, who wore blue uniform, and that Felicity she had glimpsed that night in the mirror, the girl with the flowing red-gold hair and the lips that desired to be kissed. If you had accepted that he was to share your stateroom, you know very well what might have happened, she told herself. You're not a child. But I only wanted . . . said the girl in the blue uniform. What else did you want? asked the lovely woman in the

peach-coloured negligee. I thought we would sit
up here on deck, watching the wild geese flying, his
hand in mine, and he would tell me the names of
those mountains, the snowy peaks beyond the dark
green of the forests, because I'm sure he knows them.

And then? We would have dinner together, quite
safely surrounded by people, and I would see his
eyes, golden-green, light up with laughter. And
later? We would walk about the boat deck, the vivid
light still in the sky, because we're far, far to the
north and the sun sets late, and we would talk
about his life and mine. The girl in the peach satin
laughed ironically. And every time he touched you,
even when his arm slid around your shoulders, you
would feel as if you were diving into some mysterious
whirlpool from which there was no escape. Leave
him to Crystal. She knows her way around. He's too
hard, too sophisticated for you. Diamond-hard? she
thought. That describes him, not me.

'Alone? You're looking serious. What is it you say
in English? A penny for them? Or I suppose here it
should be a dime.'

Olaf stood before her, tall and handsome with his
golden hair and beard, looking like some Viking in
his longboat on some far-off Norwegian fjord, and
she responded to the white flash of his smile with one
of her own, glad to be rid of her painful dreaming.

'My thoughts are hardly worth a dime, Olaf. Is
everything all right with you? I hope you found your
cabin comfortable.'

'No complaints. The young man is restored to his
fiancée, it seems, for the time being at least. So all is
now happiness and I don't expect to see much of
him on this trip.'

'That's good. I'm sharing a stateroom with Denise
and I don't expect to see much of her either. She's
joined the motorbike crowd.'

'So.'

The expression of Olaf's blue eyes was grave and thoughtful. Could Denise have gossiped with other passengers about the fact that presumably Felicity and Trent had planned to share a cabin? Felicity knew that, on a tour like this one, rumours could quickly spread around the whole party, or could Crystal have spread the story for some purpose of her own? Maybe she wanted to divert attention from her own plans.

'But we do not need to think of sleep yet,' said Olaf. 'Here there are hours of daylight left. Shall we take a stroll around the deck together? It would give me much pleasure.'

Felicity had imagined herself walking with Trent about the boat, but now it was with Olaf that she stepped along the deck and leaned against the rail, as the shore slipped by, clothed in mountain greenery. She tried hard to respond to Olaf's polite remarks, his obvious interest in herself rather than the passing scene, but all the time she was aware that, only a few yards away, Trent and Crystal were leaning against the rail too, and that Trent held his arm around those lovely bare shoulders as he pointed with his other hand to the dark green shores and the snowy heights beyond.

That should have been me, she thought. Oh, Felicity, how can you be so ridiculous? Forget this feeling of emptiness that comes whenever you see Trent with Crystal. This is how any woman must feel who lets him have any influence on her, because he admits himself that he could never be interested in any one woman. This attraction I had for him was nothing but a passing whim, probably increased by the fact that I refused him. And now he's turned his attentions to Crystal, who's much more beautiful, much more alluring, than I could ever hope to be.

Hope? I don't hope or want to be like Crystal, so I must stop even thinking about it. She turned with a brilliant smile to Olaf.

'Would you like to eat now? The self-service restaurant should be open and it would be best to get in early.'

She was conscious of Trent's swift glance in their direction as Olaf took her arm and they went towards the restaurant.

'Clam chowder, I think. I can't get enough of it, and poached salmon, how would that be? A little white wine perhaps?' said Olaf, as they loaded their trays.

'That sounds good.'

He's nice, she thought. A little ponderous perhaps, but his English is a bit stilted. I shouldn't encourage him, perhaps, remembering that bearlike hug, so unexpected, so embarrassing, but I can't be alone brooding, thinking too much about Trent. She could see Denise now at a table with a crowd of young people. They were making a lot of noise but seemed harmless enough, eating their hamburgers and drinking bottles of Coke. A couple of them had guitars and a squashbox.

'I don't think I need worry about Denise tonight,' she said to Olaf.

'But, my dear Felicity, why should you have to worry in any case? Her mother is here to be responsible for her.'

'She does rather seem to think she can delegate it to me,' she said.

And she herself is otherwise engaged, she thought, but did not say it.

When they came up on deck again there was no sign of Trent and Crystal. They're probably dining in Crystal's stateroom, Felicity thought. I won't see them again this evening, that's for certain, and she felt a small measure of relief at this thought. The sun was setting at last when they drew slowly towards Campbell Island and the small town of Bella Bella. It was a small town perching on the edge of the shore, great slopes of rough shale in steep slopes behind it, looking as if at any moment it could thunder down and overwhelm the little settlement.

Olaf had excused himself to try to take some photographs while the light still held, and Felicity found herself alone and yet not alone, surrounded by other people watching the small, crowded dock, full of activity. The arrival of the ferry was evidently a big event in the day and the townspeople had come to stare at the passengers just as they were being scrutinised by the tourists. Without warning she found Trent at her side, his wide shoulders pressing into the smallish space beside her. Her heart quivered tremulously as she turned to look at him.

'Did I startle you? How blue your eyes are in the waning light, Felicity. Blue as that nice fluffy sweater that is hiding those beautiful shoulders. But I preferred the gear you wore earlier—much more alluring.'

'I have no wish to allure you.' To her own ears her voice sounded stilted and prissy.

'No? Too bad. And why are you turning away from me, Felicity? Surely the charms of Bella Bella are not that riveting?'

She had turned away because she could not bear to meet the half admiring, half mocking gaze of those golden-green eyes beneath the arching dark brows. His hand, darkest brown, with its covering of gold-tipped hairs, was very close to her own on the rail. How surprised he would be if she touched it, and yet she had an overwhelming desire to slide her hand across and take his in her own.

'Why is it called Bella Bella?' she enquired, casting wildly around in her mind for something to say to hide the incredible fact of his nearness when she had thought he was with Crystal. 'I don't think it looks all that beautiful.'

'When the Hudson Bay Post was founded on Campbell Island, the Indians settled nearby, and because there were pillars built at the corners of the Hudson Bay Post, they called it Pilla Pilla, which in their pronunciation was converted to Bella Bella.'

'What an odd reason for a name. Oh, do look at that dog!'

There was a large, nondescript white dog, sitting by itself on the quayside, giving occasional excited whines and wagging its fluffy tail It riveted its gaze in one direction, obviously looking at its owner, who was presumably on the boat. But as the boat drew away again, its excitement turned to dismay as it realised its master was departing, and, over the widening stretch of water, one could hear its depressed howls sounding like a wolf in the wilderness.

'Poor thing,' said Felicity. 'What devotion!'

'Probably misplaced. The dogs on my ranch are just the same—they make a hell of a fuss when I depart. If I could possibly do without them, I would. I can dispense with that kind of idiocy whether in a dog or a woman. I've always tried to travel alone,' he added. 'No one must be utterly dependent on me for affection.'

'And you say I'm diamond-hard!' Felicity accused him.

'Ah, no, Felicity, that was just a figure of speech. You're more like an opal, cool-looking and soft as silk with hidden flashes of fire that suddenly come to the surface.'

'Opals are unlucky,' said Felicity.

'Well, a star sapphire then, with a flashing star of passion hidden deep in its heart. Oh, Felicity, you don't know what you're missing by this denial of your own glowing, sensual nature.'

I know I'm missing heartbreak, she thought.

'But perhaps you're not missing out,' Trent mused. 'Can it be that Olaf has more appeal? He certainly is a very handsome guy.'

'Yes, isn't he?' Felicity agreed. She had a wild desire to annoy him, to make him feel as she had felt when she saw his arm around Crystal's lovely shoulders. 'Those Scandinavian looks seem very appropriate to this setting, don't you think? All this is rather like the Norwegian fjords, with the pewter-coloured water and those high forested slopes.'

'And the good Olaf providing the romance, is that it? I thought I was going to be the one to do that. I could still try to prove that you've chosen the wrong man.'

'I'd rather you didn't.'

Her eyes were on his hands and she saw the brown fingers come towards hers and then, as he held her palm to his mouth, she knew the secret sensuality of his kiss, hidden as it was from the crowd of strangers around them. Only a kiss on her hand, witnessed by many, and yet it sent a flame coursing through her, reaching down to the most intimate parts of her being.

'Look at me, Felicity,' she heard him say, and then, as she turned away, not wanting to meet the gold flame of his eyes upon her, he put his hand on her chin and turned her face so that it was only inches from his own. She closed her eyes, her long lashes like a veil, hiding the disquiet this man aroused in her.

'You're deliciously shy, Felicity,' she heard him murmur. 'Don't you realise what a challenge that is to a man of my kind? Promise me one thing, Felicity. Don't trust Olaf too far.'

She could not help smiling. It's you I don't trust, she thought.

'You have no right to ask me to promise any-thing,' she said. 'I'm a free agent, and if I choose to trust Olaf, that's my affair.'

'I have the right to warn you if I feel the man won't do you any good. You are so innocent, Felicity, and yet could become most passionately involved with a man. I feel it in the very depths of me. Don't throw that away on Olaf.'

Felicity laughed. It was really most ironic that Trent should warn her against Olaf when all the time he seemed to urge her to disregard her scruples and succumb to this physical thrill she felt at his touch. But he did not realise it, and she was going to take good care that he never did know how lost to reason she felt when he was beside her.

'Do you imply that it should be thrown away on you, Trent?'

His expression was arrogant. The hand that had held her chin now stroked her face and the outline of her neck, briefly caressed the gentle curve of her breast and then became still at her waist.

'Of course, but not thrown away, Felicity. I could teach you much that you should know about love. Are you not a little curious to find out?'

'Not with you, Trent.'

His hand dropped away from her as if she had hit him and the expression of his eyes, which had been luminous with some kind of ardent persuasion, grew hard and cold.

'Can I be wrong, then? Do I repulse you so much? Do you hide such a frigid heart beneath that gentle exterior?'

She wanted to cry out, no, you're wrong. I want to be in your arms again, to experience the passion of your kiss—but something held her back. She felt he was playing with her emotions, and it was all an experiment to him. It would amuse him greatly if he knew the true state of her feelings, but what were those feelings anyway? Physical attraction, nothing more. I don't even like the man, she told herself.

'Perhaps I am frigid,' she said. 'At any rate, I don't go for shortlived affairs. Go back to Crystal. She's more your type than I am.'

Trent stepped back away from her and frowned, his eyes dark with fury.

'Maybe you're right. Of one thing you can be certain, I can't stand a jealous woman.'

'So I'm jealous as well as frigid? Well, let me tell you I couldn't possibly be jealous of Crystal because I haven't any feelings for either of you. It doesn't concern me in the least wherever you intend to spend the night.'

He laughed ironically.

'So that's it, is it? You think I intend to spend the night with Crystal?'

'Well, don't you?'

'You've just told me that you don't care whether I do or not, so I don't need to beg your forgiveness for going to someone more yielding, do I? I can tell you this much, you're a damned sight more aggravating than Crystal.'

And less attractive to you, she thought.

'Did I hear someone mention my name?' Crystal stood beside them, glowing and radiant in a jacket of ruby wool that she had slipped over the white and red sun dress. 'Oh, Felicity, do you mind very much if I take Trent away from you? I've ordered a meal in my stateroom and I must show my gratitude to your wonderful driver who seems to be able to fix anything for me, mustn't I?'

The dark anger of the expression that had been turned towards Felicity changed as Trent was drawn, not unwillingly, it seemed, away from the rail and towards the companionway. Edith, the Australian, who happened to be passing by, had evidently heard Crystal's words.

'I wonder how she intends to show her gratitude. It would surprise me if it stopped at a meal with our Belle Dame Sans Merci. She has your driver under her spell, Felicity. Don't you mind? I thought at first he rather went for you.'

'No, I hardly know him and I don't expect to meet him again after this tour. He isn't one of our regular drivers.'

'Just so long as you don't mind that man-eater having her claws into him,' said Edith.

'I don't,' said Felicity. 'They're two of a kind.'

She was glad of Edith's and Anne's company, and when presently Olaf joined them, she thought it was a good thing that she did not have to converse alone with him. He was getting too interested in her, it seemed. She told herself she certainly would not take any notice of Trent's warning. And yet, remembering Olaf's embrace, she did not want to compromise herself further with him.

The golden light stayed in the sky for a long time, but presently the water was a darker pewter and small lights bobbed on the fishing vessels that were still trawling for their catch, and there was the occasional harsh call from some seabird, winging its way back to the wooded cliffs.

'Well, now I think it's time to turn in,' said Edith, 'specially if we have to get up at dawn to see the sights.'

'Yes, I'll go too,' said Felicity.

'Stay a while longer,' Olaf pleaded, but she shook her head. The deck was becoming deserted and she did not relish the idea of a romantic scene with him.

'Perhaps a drink, or may I take you to your cabin?'

'No, really, Olaf, I have a heavy schedule ahead of me tomorrow. I'd rather not.'

He looked rather dashed, she thought. Oh, well, that couldn't be helped. Of course she was not following Trent's wishes. That would be ridiculous considering that at this moment, he and Crystal . . . better not think of it.

Of course Denise was not in the cabin. Felicity had had not expected it. But if Crystal was happy about her, why should she worry? She did not think she could come to much harm with that cheerful-looking crowd of young people, who would probably make themselves unpopular by playing their guitars and squashboxes until all hours. She could expect to be aroused somewhere in the dim hours of the morning, but maybe Denise wouldn't come to bed at all.

Felicity lay in her narrow bunk, too conscious of the throbbing engines and the creakings of the ferry-boat. She tried not to think of Trent and Crystal. Why should she? Two of a kind, she thought. Nothing to do with me. Presumably Crystal had a husband at some time, but she seems free now. Is she serious about Trent or does she just want a holiday affair? She doesn't seem the kind of woman who could be hurt as I could. Don't let me think of them. Just let me get through this tour. It will be over in a little while and then I need never see him again. I'm attracted to him physically for some insane reason, but that's not love. It can't be. He's a man who's too dangerous to love.

Finally she fell asleep, lulled now by the gentle motion of the boat, but, somewhere around four o'clock, she was roused by Denise turning on the light above her bunk and banging around in the small cabin.

'Oh, sorry, Felicity,' said Denise, surprisingly polite. 'Did I wake you? I've been having a gas time. Those guitar players are real smooth. Man, they really know where they're at!'

'I'm glad you enjoyed it,' said Felicity, yawning.

Denise was soon stretched out in brief bikini pants and exiguous bra top, breathing regularly and looking like a sleeping angel, but Felicity remained wide awake. Presently she got up quietly, changed into blue cord jeans and a striped shirt, and, putting an anorak over this, she let herself out of the cabin and made her way on to the upper deck.

There was a grey light over the waters presaging the dawn, and everything seemed very calm and still. She found herself a sheltered corner against the cool wind, and, with her hair flying behind her and her collar turned up around her chin, she stood there trying to penetrate the snow-coloured mists and see the mountains that she knew must be looming overhead. Suddenly she felt overwhelmed with a realisation that here they were surrounded by wilderness, the little trim boat, a weak representative of their civilisation, and dangers all around.

'Felicity, what are you doing here at this hour, girl?'

Trent stood beside her in a thick Cowichan sweater adorned with fierce brown eagles. His hair, damp from the mist, fell over his forehead, making him look surprisingly boyish, not at all like his usual rugged image.

'The same as you, I suppose. Peering into the mist to find the mountains.'

'Aren't you cold? I'll get us some coffee from the vending machine.'

He was off and away. While he was gone, Felicity wondered what he was doing here. Had Crystal dismissed him in case he should be seen coming out of her stateroom later? Maybe.

'Here we are,' he said, coming back with two steaming cups of coffee. 'Why are you awake so early? I thought you advised that we needed rest.'

'I couldn't sleep, and I can't imagine that you ever tire.'

With that lock of hair falling over his brow he looked somehow not as hard as usual. There was something gentler about his mouth. Was that the effect of his night with Crystal? If Crystal could do that to him. . . . Felicity was surprised to feel a swift stab of pain somewhere in the vicinity of her breast.

Despite her protests, Trent wrapped his anorak around them both as they sipped the hot coffee.

'No, that's true,' he said, answering her previous remark. 'I have enormous stores of energy. I doubt whether any woman could keep up with me.'

He said it simply, not boasting, merely stating a fact. How infuriating he could be, she thought, how arrogant! He really was impossible. So why did the bulk of him, pressed against her in this little space, produce such a feeling of suffocating excitement, a feeling of danger, like that thrill of fear she had sensed alone with those mountains and forests crowding in on her?

Suddenly there was an eerie roar quite near to the boat, an unearthly sound that echoed over the still grey water.

'Oh, what's that?'

She had started nervously and Trent put his arm around her and held her hand as if to calm her. How dared he touch her when he had come straight from Crystal? And yet she was glad of that reassuring feel of his large bulk beside her.

'Some sea-lions,' he said, and, where he pointed, she could now see the seal-like heads bobbing around above the surface, staring with avid curiosity at the boat. There were some half a dozen of them, gazing in their direction with curiously human, large dark eyes.

'How innocent they look,' Felicity exclaimed. 'One can't imagine anyone ever wanting to harm them.

They seem to go in with the landscape, wilderness creatures, even in the water.'

'The fishermen wouldn't share your view of their innocence. They eat quantities of fish, but here I guess there's plenty and to spare for man and beast.'

'It's such a wonderful country, like one's idea of Paradise—except of course you can't imagine Paradise with snow on the mountains, but you can imagine what heaven it must have been for the Indians before the white man came—everything provided, food to eat, fish, berries, game, bark of trees to make shelters and garments. What a good life!'

'And other tribes to fight and bears to hug you,' said Trent, grinning. 'No, no, I shouldn't bring down your idealistic view, should I?'

'I don't believe it is idealistic. It must have been marvellous here. It still is.'

'Look,' said Trent.

Beyond the basking sea-lions, who were totally engrossed in satisfying their curiosity about the boat and its inhabitants, Felicity could see a flurry in the calm water, and then she gasped. A pod of killer whales, streamlined black and white, surfaced almost simultaneously, advancing in arching formation. All at once the sea-lions must have spotted them and dived hurriedly.

'There, you see. Killers are all around us here as well as in the city.'

'They're beautiful even if they are killers,' said Felicity. 'And there must be that kind of creature to restore the balance of nature.'

'What a calm person you are, Felicity, seeing good even in a killer whale. You're not easily shaken, are you? Most women would have been terrifically alarmed at the sight of all those whales.'

I am easily shaken, she thought, but fortunately I seem to be able to disguise it from Trent.

'I have to have a placid disposition if I'm to run tours such as this,' she said. 'It wouldn't do to throw a fit of temperament whenever anything went wrong.'

Trent smiled. He was so close to her that she caught again the woodsy fragrance of his aftershave.

'That's a challenge too. I have a great ambition to make you lose your cool, my unimpassioned Felicity.'

And you have the ability to do just that, she thought.

'You can always try,' she said.

'Is that an invitation?'

She felt a shuddering thrill of mingled terror and delight as his mouth sought hers, and she felt him unzipping her anorak, seeking the slope of her waist, curving his brown hand to take the shape of her breast. The moment seemed to stretch into hours, standing there in the misty dawn, seeming alone on this boat as it ploughed its smooth passage over the water with wilderness on either side. And then he let her go. Over his shoulder she could see that the mists had gone and the first soft rays of early morning sunlight were reflecting off the snow-capped mountain peaks, rosy in the dawn.

'There, wasn't that good?'

She put her hand to her mouth that felt bruised by his kisses. His eyes, looking down into hers, had the golden animal glow of some creature of the wilderness. She was truly terrified by the emotions this man could arouse in her. For those few moments she had wanted to yield, to give herself up entirely to some desperate enchantment of the senses. She must not let him know. She must hold on to some kind of sanity and not give way to this mad desire to tread the wildly dangerous route to heartbreak. Crystal, she thought. He was with Crystal last night.

'No, it was not!' she cried. 'It wasn't good. How

dare you come to me and try to make love to me
when you know that only minutes ago you've come
from Crystal's stateroom? You're truly the most impossible, arrogant man I've ever met in my life. I
want nothing to do with you. Keep your kisses for
her!'

Now his eyes, looking down at her, were in-
scrutable, and yet a small fire flickered in their dark
depths. He lifted his head to the snowy peaks and
seemed to shake himself, looking, she thought, with
his aquiline profile, like an angel, glorying in its
own strength.

'So that's what you think of me. You obviously
made up your mind to hate me from the start. And
still your lips hold so much promise. We could have
been wonderful for each other. But so be it. What a
little fool you are, Felicity.'

She heard his footsteps receding away from her as
she leaned on the rail, her head bowed. Well, now
perhaps it was over, something that had never really
begun. Trent would not worry her again. She gazed
at the glory of the mountains, rosy in the morning
light, so beautiful it made her want to weep. Oh, yes,
she told herself, that was why her face was wet. There
could be no other reason.

CHAPTER EIGHT

So here they were, driving out of Prince Rupert
with the exciting Inner Passage part of the tour behind them. The short break from her duties was over
and she had not had the rest she had anticipated, but
it could not be helped. Felicity looked at the back of
Trent's head, the strong neck, the wavy dark brown

hair, and, as he edged his way cautiously from the ferryboat on to the dock and away on to the road that was to lead to the Yellowhead Highway, once more she wished that this had been a normal trip and that she had never even heard of such a person as Trent Seymour.

Her head ached slightly and her eyes felt heavy, but her passengers seemed to have gained a new lease of life from the boat trip and were chattering like a cage full of jaybirds. All except Crystal and Denise. Crystal, pale and elegant in a lavender slacks suit, looked out of the window of the coach with not a glance in Trent's direction. Denise, doubtless still tired after her lack of sleep, dozed in her seat, looking quite beautiful with her long lashes and sulky mouth. Well, thought Felicity, too bad she would probably disturb Denise, but she must do her duty as a tour operator and give the others some information. That was what she was paid for. She switched on her speaker.

'Prince Rupert, the town we've just left, has the third largest natural harbour in the world. Fortunately it's free from ice all the year round. The port is used for transporting lumber, grain, ore and fish products, and it's the halibut capital of the world.

'On your right, you have the Skeena River. It has its source in the high peaks of the Northern British Columbia mountains, born from the mist and clouds and rain and snow. As it plunges down to the Pacific, it gathers into itself the waters from hundreds of other streams. The Indians called it the River Ksan, but English explorers called it Skeena when they tried to pronounce it. It really means, "Water of the Clouds". The river with its lakes and streams provided a rich life for fish and animals long before man came on the scene, and the Indians had appreciated the good things this valley provided long before the white man arrived. There are Pacific salmon, steelhead, rainbow cut-throat and many more, great forests and lush grasslands, and lots of animals too.

'The people who lived here called themselves the Gitskan, People of the Ksan. They had an assured food supply with ample fish and wild life, so they had plenty of leisure to develop their own art. And that's what I'm taking you to see today, an Indian village that's been made as a replica of what used to exist here. There are people there still practising the skills they used such a long time ago. Gitskan art was mainly one of intricate design and form worked in red cedar, birch, alder, and beautifully carved arti- facts in stone have also been found. This art practi- cally disappeared when the white man took over, because the Indians wanted the things they were offered for trading and in exchange they trapped for furs, and, doing this, they didn't have so much leisure, so they stopped making all these beautiful objects.

'However, fortunately some interested people managed to retrieve some of the old art forms and thought of making a museum, but that seemed too dead, and so the idea of a living Indian village was formed, so that people could come and see how things used to be. As well as housing the old things, it has be- come a place where people who are still gifted can find an outlet for the art they practise. You'll see they have very many interesting goods for sale there.'

'What kind of things?'

Denise, who had been yawning in a very bored kind of way, suddenly brightened up at the idea of being able to buy something.

'All kinds of things made from wood, gold, silver, copper. Carvings, boxes, masks, ear-rings, bracelets, cufflinks.'

'Sounds great,' said Edith, and Anne agreed.

They were driving along the broad highway with the Skeena River on their right, full of snow water, green and cold, but to their left now were great slabs of cliff, where the moss looked so green it was incandescent, and the rocks were fissured with gulleys where waterfalls dashed themselves, kamikazi style, upon the shores below. In one place the coach went over a bridge with the river hundreds of feet underneath it.

'All the time this country becomes more, how do you say, spectacular,' said Olaf.

I should be enjoying it, thought Felicity. I would have enjoyed it if only Trent hadn't been here to torment me, to disturb me, to get under my skin. Why do I let him upset me so? I must try to ignore him.

And now they came to the Ksan village, situated at the junction of the Skeena and Bulkley Rivers with the rugged Rocher Deboule range in the distance across the water.

'Mountain of Rolling Stones,' said Felicity, as she handed her passengers out of the coach. 'I wonder how it got its name.'

'Doubtless there were many sore heads or worse to show it was a good one,' said Trent.

He too was helping people out of the coach and now he smiled at her, that heartcatching smile that seemed to melt the icy splinter in her heart, and it was just as if the scene at dawning had never happened.

The day had fulfilled its dawn promise and the sun was bright, lending its warm glow to make the village on the banks of the Skeena look even more picturesque.

'This is really something,' said Edith as they saw the six houses with the huge totem poles, carved with strange beasts, towering up beside them. They were met by an Indian hostess who proceeded to show them around, explaining clearly the function of each building.

'The first house is the Frog House of the Distant Past. It shows Gitskan life in pre-European times; the heavy posts and planking are hand-adzed as they would have been in the old days.'

A dozen life-size figures portrayed various activities of the period. A woman and girl were weaving a mat and rain cloak from cedar bark. A medicine man in full regalia was curing a patient. A chief and his wife in all their most splendid clothes were preparing a grand feast, around them boxes, ladles, food dishes and furs.

'The second house is the Wolf House of the Grandfathers. This brings us to the time of the arrival of the traders, and so you see copper goods, cast-iron kettles, brass kerosene lamps. We sometimes have ceremonial dancing here.'

'That great painted screen on the wall must make a wonderful backdrop for the dancing,' said Felicity.

'Yes, it does. It features the Wolf Crest in traditional design.'

'That wolf looks pretty fierce,' said Trent. In the semi-darkness of the hut, he had drawn near to Felicity without her realising it, and now he put his hand on her arm, smoothing the hollow of her elbow. 'But then all wolves are, aren't they, Felicity? Human as well as animal.'

She could see the glint of laughter and the white flash of his smile. Why must he torment her so? She had thought this morning that she had finished with him because she had made him angry, but here he was up to his tricks again.

'You will see,' said the hostess, 'that the old customs and ceremonies were still in effect. Here are

two figures clothed in their regalia but, unlike the
ones in the Frog House, the chief wearing his robe of
skin, this chief has a beautiful button blanket, the
kind that is still in use today.'

Felicity moved away from Trent on a pretence of
looking at the blanket that was intricately patterned
with hundreds of white pearl buttons, and she saw
Crystal glance sharply in their direction. Had he had
some difference with Crystal, she wondered, and
was he playing herself against the other woman?

They visited the House of Treasures that had a
collection of antique Gitskan artifacts, cherished
objects, handed down, and now housed safely here
for visitors to admire, and they saw exquisite basketwork, carvings, soft moose leather garments, beaded
in intricate patterns. And finally they came to the
Today House of the Arts, where there were beautiful
objects for sale made by modern craftsmen in the style
handed down from generation to generation, at one
time thought lost, but now revived again. There was
exquisite basketwork, weird, colourful masks, carvings of whales and other beasts, intricately worked
boxes and jewellery, silver ear-rings, cufflinks, bracelets, all finely carved with meaningful symbols.

Felicity lingered a long time here, admiring the
work of the craftsmen. She could not imagine that
she would ever want to adorn her home with the
terrifying masks, but the carving was very skilled and
the boxes were interesting objects to have around,
but most of all she admired the fine work upon the
jewellery. This she could understand and appreciate.

Trent found her poring over an exquisitely
wrought gold bracelet.

'Try it on,' he said.

The temptation was great. The bracelet had a gap
so that it could fit any wrist.

'Do you think I should?' she asked nervously. 'I

couldn't possibly afford it.'

'There's no harm in trying it.'

She put it on. Against the golden colour of her arm the bracelet glowed, fitting as if it had been specially made for her.

'Oh, how lovely it is!' she exclaimed.

Trent suddenly smiled.

'So you have some natural feminine reactions in spite of your calm, cool nature, my Felicity.'

I'm not your Felicity, she thought rebelliously. Nor am I cool and calm, but you're not to know that, and never will, I hope.

'I see a covetous gleam in those lovely blue eyes. Allow me to buy it for you.'

She drew back, taking the bracelet from her arm as if it had been a snake wound there.

'Oh, no, Trent, I couldn't possibly!'

'Why ever not? Most women would jump at the chance.'

'But I'm not most women. No, Trent, I couldn't possibly accept such a valuable present from you or any other man.'

'Valuable? A few hundred dollars, neither here nor there. I'm not offering you a diamond necklace. Look at it this way. Through you I'm having an experience that's novel and amusing to me and a complete relaxation from my usual hectic way of life. Don't you deserve some reward for that?'

'It's not my fault you're here,' she pointed out. 'I never wanted you here in the first place. This is all your own doing. You're under no obligation to me and I have no intention of being under an obligation to you. So I couldn't possibly accept a gold bracelet from you. Please understand that, Trent.'

The smile had gone from his eyes.

'I understand that well enough. Thank you for spelling out your dislike of me in such simple terms.

And as for the bracelet, forget it. Obviously you're determined to be as ungracious as possible. Well, let it be.'

A cloud seemed to have gathered over the bright day as Felicity assembled her passengers to go on their way, and they drove on to Smithers, a small, spread out sort of town with low mountains around it and wide streets, the kind where you could have turned a team of horses in days gone by.

When she had settled her tourists in their various rooms, she accepted an invitation from Anne and Edith to come out and have a hamburger with them. She was waiting for them in the foyer of the motel in her blue jeans, striped T-shirt and towelling jacket, when Crystal stepped out from the elevator. As usual, she looked extremely elegant in an intricately cut dress of crêpe, the colour of autumn bracken. She carried a stole of fine mesh gold thread and her high strappy sandals of gold kid looked somehow unsuitable for the streets of this country town. In fact the whole outfit would have been more at home in New York.

'Oh, hello, Felicity, isn't Trent here yet? How remiss of him! He's usually so attentive. I asked him to come out to dinner with me. He's such good company, isn't he? Denise is having a hamburger in her room. Unfortunately she has the sulks again. Misses young people around her, I guess. And where are you off to?'

'I'm going to some Hamburger Heaven with Edith and Anne.'

'How thrilling! By the way, I hope I'm not breaking anything up between you two.'

'Us two?' asked Felicity.

'You and Trent,' explained Crystal. 'Now don't play the innocent with me, Felicity. I guess it's usual on a trip like this for the courier and driver to

get together—that is, if they can't find any other
diversions.'

'No, it's far from usual,' Felicity said coolly.

So go ahead, she wanted to say. Take him out to
dinner, and I wish you joy of him. Just then Trent
arrived down in the escalator. His cream silk shirt
under the soft tan shade jacket showed off the
bronzed features, the golden green of his eyes.

'Oh, there you are, Trent. Here's Felicity going
out to grab a hamburger with Anne and Edith.
Doesn't she look charming in her jeans?'

Trent hardly glanced in Felicity's direction.

'I've ordered a cab, Crystal. It should be outside
any moment now. Let's go.'

Crystal adjusted the gold stole and put a hand on
Trent's arm. As she did so, Felicity felt an accelera-
tion of the beat of her heart. On that arm, now
linked so possessively with Trent's, was the gold
bracelet, the one she had coveted for her own, the one
that Trent had offered to her.

'You're very quiet,' Edith commented as they sat
perched on red stools, eating French fries and double
hamburgers liberally laced with ketchup. 'Are you
exhausted?'

'Not at all,' Felicity assured her. 'My mind was on
something I had to think out. Sorry I'm not better
company.'

'Think nothing of it. You must have a lot on your
mind having to organise us all.'

'It's not that,' said Felicity.

'Are you worried about your driver being eaten
alive by the lovely Crystal, then?'

'Oh, no. I'm sure he can take care of himself in
any circumstances. The only thing is the company
disapproves highly of any suggestion of romance
between staff and passengers.'

'Too bad. How about Olaf, then? I'd say he's

taken quite a shine to you, Felicity.'

'Oh, I don't think so.'

Felicity shook her head emphatically. I have enough on my mind, she thought, without thinking about Olaf. Why do you feel so depressed? she asked herself. You were offered the bracelet and you refused it. Trent had every right to give it to anyone else he chose. Was I ungracious as he said? But how could I have accepted any gift from him without it meaning something significant? I'm not like Crystal, who could accept a gift like that as casually as Trent would give it. But Trent would laugh at my scruples. He thinks I'm prim and puritanical—and I'm not. Oh, Trent, how could you give to Crystal the bracelet I would have prized so much?

Back in her room, she showered and put on her pale blue tailored pyjamas and the blue towelling robe that matched the suit. She was just about to get into bed with some reading matter, when the phone rang on the bedside table.

'Felicity, this is Olaf. Won't you come to my room for a drink? Edith and Anne are here. They said you wouldn't be asleep yet.'

Why not? thought Felicity. Trent said I should beware of Olaf. That's a laugh, isn't it? If Edith and Anne are there, I'll be quite safe from Olaf's meaningful looks and I know I'm not going to be able to sleep if I do go to bed. A drink might help me to sleep. The sensible Felicity said to her, it isn't just because you're hurt with Trent over the bracelet that you want to go to have a drink with Olaf, is it? Of course not, she replied to this other self.

She had half expected to hear Edith's cheerful laugh as she came along the corridor to Olaf's room, but all was quiet, when she knocked at the door. Olaf opened to her, smiling in a very welcoming fashion.

'How lovely to have you here! Thank you for fulfilling my dearest wish. I desired it so much that you would come.'

Felicity was rather startled by this effusive greeting.

'But where are Anne and Edith?' she asked. 'You said they were here with you?'

Olaf shrugged his shoulders and spread out his hands in a dismissive gesture.

'No, no, I thought to ask them and then I thought better not. You are disappointed not to have them here? You must excuse me. It was just my little joke. Not a good one, perhaps, but I thought you might not come if you knew we were to be alone, but me, I was feeling lonely, and it is the courier's duty to look after her passengers' welfare, no?'

No, thought Felicity, it is certainly not my duty to look after your welfare at this time of life, Olaf. However, now I'm here I'd better put a good face on things. She felt embarrassed that she had come here so stupidly in her pyjamas and robe. She would never have done so if she had not thought that Edith and Anne were to be here and that they were just to have a sociable half hour or so.

'You will have a drink with me, no?'

In his hand Olaf was holding a bottle of French champagne that he had plucked from its nest of ice.

'Oh, no, Olaf, please not champagne at this time of night! If I could have a Coke or a glass of milk, that would be splendid.'

Olaf's face fell.

'I thought all women loved champagne.'

'At weddings and important celebrations, Olaf. Not just as a casual nightcap. I'd wake with a headache and, for this tour, I need to have all my wits about me. I'm very sorry.'

He looked so downcast that she felt guilty.

'I thought maybe this was to be some kind of celebration. One moment, Felicity, I must go to the dispenser at the end of the corridor to fetch you this milk.'

What did he mean? she wondered when she was left alone. Really, she had been unutterably foolish to find herself in this situation. She vowed that she would just drink her milk and then excuse herself. Remembering that clumsy embrace of his, she felt a small qualm of uneasiness that she had come at all. It had been deceitful of him to say Anne and Edith were here. She would not have thought him capable of lying to gain his own ends. And what were those ends? She remembered Trent's warning not to get involved with Olaf. Really, that had been too ridiculous.

Trent? She thought of him and Crystal, dining somewhere romantic, then coming back to the hotel to have a last drink together. It would not worry Trent to be drinking champagne even if he had to make an early start tomorrow. Oh, why did he give that lovely bracelet to Crystal? she thought. Was it in gratitude for the previous night? Why couldn't he have given her something else, not the same gift he'd offered to me?

'Here we are,' announced Olaf. 'A beaker of milk instead of champagne. You are a strange girl, Felicity.'

'Thank you, Olaf, that's great. What was the celebration you were talking about? It isn't your birthday?'

Olaf laughed.

'Nothing like that. I hoped the celebration would be between you and me.'

'I don't understand.'

'Dear Felicity, are you as innocent as you look? I had thought that you and I had become friends on this tour.'

'I think we have,' said Felicity.

Olaf smiled. He really was extremely handsome, thought Felicity, with his muscular frame, his halo of golden curls and his sea-blue eyes under their bushy lashes.

'Then why not let it go a stage further? Stay here with me tonight. I think we could make each other very happy.'

Felicity hoped she did not look as astonished as she felt. Olaf, whom she had thought so friendly but so polite! She would not have dreamed that he was capable of such a proposition, and with so little encouragement on her part. So Trent could be right. She put her beaker of milk down upon the table and rose to her feet.

'I'm sorry, Olaf, you've made a mistake. I feel friendly towards you, certainly, but not that friendly.' She felt she must try to pass this off without offending him. 'I'll go now.'

She made to go to the door, but he was surprisingly quick for such a large man, and with a swift movement, stood between her and her escape.

'But you encouraged me by this friendship to think you might like to go further. You accepted my kiss. And what am I to think when you come to my room at this hour, dressed as you are?'

'But you said Anne and Edith were here.'

'You cannot have believed that tale in your heart. You must have known it was just an excuse.'

'No, I did not!' she snapped.

'Oh, why waste time in talking? This should convince you more adequately.'

Now she felt herself enveloped in his strong arms, a stifling embrace that was like being wrapped around in steel bands. His face came down towards her and she felt the silky strength of his beard as she turned her head this way and that to escape his kisses. She felt one large hand groping beneath the towelling robe, feeling for the buttons that were a frail defence against his assault. She wanted to scream and yet something held her back and she struggled silently against the unrelenting power of this large man. Vaguely she remembered some advice she had once been given: 'Don't scream if you are attacked, rather save your strength to resist. Use your feet to kick your assailant.'

With all her might, she kicked out at Olaf. He was caught temporarily off balance and, in that small movement, she managed to slip away and make for the door.

'I'm sorry, Olaf, you had the wrong idea,' she gasped, before she slammed it shut behind her.

He would not follow her into the corridor, she was sure of that. She paused to get her breath back and to tighten the belt of her robe. What a fool she had been! But who would have thought it of Olaf, who had always been so polite in his dealings with her? But there had been that one embrace, the one Trent had witnessed. I should have known, she reproached herself. She made her way towards the bend of the corridor, and then halted, startled. Trent and Crystal were standing near the drinks dispenser, staring in her direction. They had evidently just come up the escalator and had stopped to get something from the vendor, and they had seen her coming from Olaf's room, looking totally dishevelled! But perhaps they did not know it was Olaf's room.

Her hope was in vain. Crystal looked her up and down, her catlike eyes seeming to take in every detail of Felicity's appearance.

'Been visiting Olaf, Felicity? That is his room, isn't it? You do take your duties seriously to offer kindnesses at this late hour, don't you?'

Trent did not say a word. Felicity glanced swiftly

at him. His expression was mysterious, enigmatic, his eyes green as snow water. What was he thinking? Oh, Trent, she wanted to say, how right, how infuriatingly right you were to warn me against Olaf!

CHAPTER NINE

IF Felicity had been afraid she had offended Olaf, she need not have worried. Next morning on the coach he greeted her as if nothing untoward had happened. Felicity decided that she must just try to forget about the whole incident. She herself must take some of the blame for accepting his invitation so late at night without thinking of the implications. Olaf seemed at the moment to be making himself agreeable to Crystal and Denise. Well, that was all to the good. Perhaps if he could improve his acquaintance with some of the other passengers, it would cure his loneliness.

Trent, on the other hand, appeared cool in the extreme. He had hardly looked at Felicity when they were consulting together about the day's journey. She wanted to take him aside, to convince him that she had not gone to Olaf's room for any amorous purpose, but she realised that would be difficult. Appearances were against her. And what, after all, had it to do with Trent? He's not my keeper, she told herself, and how can he reproach me with anything when he came to me the other morning straight from Crystal's stateroom?

This morning they were to visit a fossil field where it was possible to pick up souvenirs quite easily. If they were not of any great importance, visitors were allowed to keep them. So after leaving the coach, the party made their way there, walking through woodlands with tall trees and wild flowers beside the path, scarlet aquilegia and tall pale lavender blossoms and Indian paintbrushes, brightly scarlet, all thrusting their way up among the green of the ferns.

Through the trees a wide, shallow stream gurgled its way between grassy banks, with here and there a waterfall bubbling over the stones. Crystal had elected to stay in the coach. She said she couldn't care less about finding fossils, but Denise came along and, rather to Felicity's surprise, Olaf walked with her, engaging her in conversation that seemed to involve quite a deal of laughter on both their parts. Felicity had thought that Trent might stay with Crystal and probably Crystal had thought that too when she planned to stay, but maybe for once Trent had become conscientious about his duties, for she found he was walking beside her as they negotiated the narrow path.

'How are you, Felicity? You look tired.'

She was surprised by this comment and looked up, wide-eyed, at the craggy profile presented to her.

'You have pale lavender shadows under those blue, blue eyes. Not unbecoming, I must say. What happened last night?'

'Not what you think.'

'How do you know what I think?'

'Really, Trent, it has nothing whatever to do with you!' Felicity exclaimed. 'However, I'll tell you. Olaf asked me to his room for a late-night drink. He told me Edith and Anne were there.'

'And they were not. Very convenient for Olaf that you were willing to believe such a tale.'

'Why shouldn't I?'

'No reason except of course it's been obvious to me from the start that Olaf is violently attracted to you.

And all's fair . . . you know the rest. Sometimes you behave very foolishly, Felicity. You can't say I didn't warn you. So what happened?'

Felicity felt herself blushing.

'I'd rather not say. Really, Trent, you're not my keeper!'

'Take it easy!' he grinned. 'I must say when you came out of that room, you scarcely looked like a woman fulfilled, more like a kitten that's just escaped a large, clumsy dog.'

She could not help laughing.

'That's just about it! But, Trent, if Olaf was violently attracted to me, as you said, he isn't now. Just look at him with Denise!'

The two of them were walking along the path, hand in hand, and Olaf was laughing at something Denise had just said.

'That should keep both of them out of mischief,' said Trent with some satisfaction.

He himself pretends to be attracted to me, thought Felicity, but how can he be? He wasn't even jealous when he saw me coming out of Olaf's room. Is that because he's so arrogant that he can't believe any woman could be attracted to another man when he himself is on the scene? No, he doesn't feel anything for me. It's all a cat-and-mouse game to him. It would amuse him to seduce me. I wonder if he chalks up his conquests on the side of his plane? A pin-up girl crossed out. He's capable of anything.

Her thoughts were interrupted when they arrived at the fossil field, a steep bank of shale with loose rocks around. The party set to with a will, tapping stones together to split them, and quite soon there were cries of triumph as occasionally this revealed some fossil hidden up until now for a million years. Upon the grey flat stones there were ferns that had been pressed there all those aeons of time away and images of skeletal fish, even the silhouettes of flies that looked remarkably like mosquitoes. Trent was the expert. He had obviously had experience of something like this before and he made himself very popular by presenting his finds to those who had failed to find any for themselves.

Felicity had not joined in the search. After she had conducted her party there, she found a tall tree and sat with her back resting against its trunk, surrounded by the wild flowers of the forest, listening to the sound of water bubbling over stones. Yes, she was weary, as Trent had said, and she was only halfway through the tour. No wonder the tour operators made the strict rule of no romance! Even the emotion she had expended on Trent had been exhausting, and that was certainly not romantic, rather a constant thorn in the flesh, a nagging pain. She felt her head nodding. She should not sleep while on duty, should she? But, here in the forest, with the warm sun filtering through the trees and the buzzing sound of insects on the wing, she could not keep her eyes open. She slipped sideways into a lying position and her heavy lids closed.

She awoke reluctantly, aroused by some gentle touch upon her face. Could it have been one of those coloured butterflies working so energetically at sucking the nectar from the rose-pink flowers? Oh, no, it was more than that. Above the fragrance of the grasses, she was aware once more of that woodsy scent, and now she felt Trent's well remembered mouth passing over the planes of her face until it reached her own. For some moments she lay in delicious indolence, tasting the warmth of his mouth upon hers, surrendering to the throbbing waves of desire that blazed from that touch. And then she opened her eyes and stared into the green depths of his, so close that she could see each separate golden fleck and every curling black lash below the dark brows. She sat up suddenly and the leaves and flowers spun for a moment in a dizzy kaleidoscope of reds and pinks and greens before settling down into a more sober pattern.

'Where are the others? How long have I been sleeping?'

His arm was still around her, supporting her with his strength, his mouth, inches away from her own, now wandered across her face and down to where the low-cut T-shirt revealed the slight curves of her breasts.

'Don't panic,' he said softly. 'They're picnicking by the river. We left you to rest. You were sleeping so soundly.'

'Oh, I shouldn't have slept!' exclaimed Felicity. 'What will they think of me?'

'Not to worry. I was there.'

Although his arm was still around her, his caresses had ceased now that she was properly awake. She felt as if she had dreamed it, imagined those sensations that had been so wonderful for so short a time. Oh, how was it that this man, who often aroused such anger in her, could make her feel like this?

'And look what I've found for you. Or won't you take even this from me?'

Dazedly she looked at what Trent had in his hand. It was a fossil of a shell, curling in complete and perfect pattern, in convoluted whorls.

'Oh, how lovely!' she exclaimed.

'It's like you, Felicity, like that mysterious inner self you have, the intricate workings of your mind that make you very hard to know. Will you take it?'

'Oh, yes, please!'

It will remind me of this day always, remind me of Trent. But do I want to be reminded? she asked herself.

'Strange girl, you prefer this bit of stone to that gold bracelet,' said Trent.

It's more valuable to me, she thought—but oh, Trent, don't remind me of the bracelet.

'Let's go to join the others,' she said. 'They must be wondering where we are.'

However, her party seemed quite contented to be out of the coach and enjoying a picnic alfresco by the banks of the sparkling river. They had shopped at a supermarket this morning and bought bread rolls, cheese, pâté and salami with tomatoes and lettuce, and now they pooled their resources, drinking cans of beer and of orange juice. Al and Mary Lou were quite reconciled now, Felicity was pleased to note. Denise was chatting animatedly to Olaf. The rest of the coach load, Hollanders, Australians, Canadians and British, were by now on first name terms and seemed happy exchanging gossip about their lives.

Only Crystal seemed to hold aloof. In her elegant lavender slacks suit, she seemed a creature from a distant world. Why, wondered Felicity, had she come in the first place? This kind of rather matey coach trip didn't seem her scene at all. She looked coldly at Felicity and Trent as they reappeared on the scene, and Felicity felt that Trent's kisses were imprinted on her mouth for all the world to see. She left him and hastened to make the rounds of the passengers, chatting to people, bringing in any who seemed to be a little apart from the rest. And soon she saw that Trent was with Crystal again, and that those violet eyes were gazing up into his own with devastating appeal.

Now Denise leapt to her feet, dragging Olaf with her.

'How gorgeous that pool looks, just right for a dip. I'm so hot, I could die. How about it, everyone? Who's for a swim?'

Edith and Anne objected.

'We shouldn't have eaten first if we intended to swim. It's too soon after lunch.'

'Oh, phooey, it won't do us any harm,' said Denise.

But the others declined. They had eaten well and the beer had made them sleepy.

'Such a lot of fuddy-duddys,' Felicity heard Denise mutter, and with that she flung off the sundress she had been wearing and stood there in brief bikini pants and black lace bra, then she ran to the pool and lowered herself into the water, splashing out to swim to the farther side, where the stream tumbled in over the rocks.

'Come in, Olaf, it's gorgeous!' she shouted, but even Olaf seemed reluctant to take up her invitation. Probably, thought Felicity, he was reluctant to go in without a proper swimsuit in front of all this crowd.

Not that the others were very interested in the sight of Denise disporting herself. The picnic party presented a picture of noontide somnolence, most of them lying back in the shade, hats over their faces. Only Olaf was watching Denise intently. Trent was occupied with Crystal, and Felicity was gathering up the remains of the meal, but she glanced up once to see that Denise had moved away from the pool, swimming through a gap in the rocks to find herself in the open stream. She seemed to be a strong swimmer, but nevertheless Felicity watched her with growing anxiety, for the river seemed fast flowing, and deeper in parts than it had looked at first.

Suddenly Denise threw up her hands and screamed.

'Help me! I can't get back!'

Her shouts were muffled as she was turned over and over, being swept by the current towards the middle of the stream and the deeper part. The peaceful scene was suddenly disrupted by panic as people ran towards the bank in futile attempts to give advice. Crystal screamed hysterically and held on to Trent, hiding her face against his shoulder. Olaf was nearest to the spot where Denise had been swimming and, flinging off his outer clothes, he struck out strongly across the fast running water. Trent meanwhile, roughly disengaging himself from Crystal's hysterical grasp, ran farther downstream along the bank and plunged, fully clothed, into the foaming torrent. It was he who caught the frightened girl and dragged her to the bank, but Olaf went to help them and took over the burden as they came towards him, and it was to him that she clung as she sobbed and coughed, then, quietening down, smiled seraphically at him, not even seeming to realise that it had been Trent who rescued her in the first place.

'Oh, Olaf, that's the second time you've rescued me. How about that? You really are a hero!'

She clung to him, smiling up into his eyes. By this time Crystal had arrived and was watching the scene, looking on rather helplessly. Felicity meanwhile had gone back to the coach to fetch a towel, but Olaf took it from her and proceeded to dry Denise, an operation that she seemed to enjoy. She sat in the sun, briefly clad in her damp underwear, her wet hair streaming in waving curls around her, and appeared to be revelling in all the attention she was getting.

Crystal rounded on Felicity.

'This is the second time that Denise has been in mortal danger. I thought you were supposed to take care of the people who are in your charge.'

'So I am,' said Felicity.

But my duty doesn't include looking after a headstrong teenager whose mother doesn't seem capable of keeping her in order, she thought, but did not say so, for she was still feeling very shaken by the whole affair.

'She could easily have drowned,' said Crystal.

'But I didn't,' said Denise. 'Thanks to Olaf again. Isn't he something? It was great the way he just came in after me.'

She leaned back against Olaf and looked up at him with her melting brown eyes.

'Oh-oh,' said Edith. 'The man-eating cub has got her sights on your admirer, Felicity.'

'He isn't my admirer. I'd be glad if he'd make friends with others in the party.'

But all the same, she thought, Olaf shouldn't get too interested in Denise. She's too much like a butterfly, settling on any male who attracts her but never staying for long. However, if it keeps them happy during the trip, I shouldn't grumble. Olaf is old enough to know what he's doing.

When Olaf and Trent had changed into dry things, the coach proceeded on its way towards Prince George. Everyone seemed to have recovered from the shock of Denise's accident, more especially Denise herself. She sat next to Olaf now, chatting to him in a very animated fashion, but Crystal sat alone, her lovely face closed up and brooding.

Felicity wondered whether she was still blaming her. She seemed to hold her responsible for everything that happened, even things that were quite out of her control. Why has she got such a grudge against me? thought Felicity. Does she think of me as a rival for Trent's affections? But surely she holds all the cards. She's so beautiful, so sophisticated, just the kind of woman Trent would like to be seen with. He said so himself. I'm a kind of joke to him. It amuses him to play with me. He's come into my world for a kind of whim, and soon he'll be gone again.

Felicity looked out at the changing scenery along the Yellowhead Highway. There were wide farmlands with yellow flowering pastures, spangled with white daisies, full of rich herds of cattle, red shorthorns and Friesians. There were squat, odd-shaped barns, wooden houses, little primitive churches, and, all along the road, bushes of pink roses rioting in glorious profusion, graceful white-barked poplar trees, very tall and thin, and white eyes of daisies in the green of the grass.

'Spring can be treacherous here,' said Trent. 'It's good ranching country but dicey for growing trees. You can get an early warm spell and then a sudden cold snap. The sap rises in the first heat of the sun and then a sudden frost occurs and it freezes in the bark.'

That's the effect you have on me, Trent, thought Felicity. Your touch, your smile can delight me, thrill me into warm surrender, then something you do or say is like a sudden frost that chills my veins.

'Next stop Prince George,' she said to her passengers. 'And after that the most exciting part of the tour begins—the great national parks, Jasper and Banff, but first, Mount Robson, one of the highest peaks.'

CHAPTER TEN

Now that they were into the National Parks, they felt they were really in the Rockies. Mount Robson seemed to welcome them, thrusting up its high peak in a sky of clearest blue, eternal snows upon its ancient heights. When they reached Jasper National Park, there seemed to be forested mountains all around them; dark cedars, lighter hemlock, spruce and fir gave the effect of a green patchwork on the lower slopes. They saw Moose Lake, looking very green and cold. Rivers, waterfalls, high mountains with white descending glaciers, all passed before their fascinated gaze. This at last seemed the heart of what they had come so far to see.

At Jasper, the travellers seemed glad to have arrived in a town, somewhere where they could sightsee at leisure and do some shopping as well. The first day Felicity did a tour of the region with them in the coach, but the second afternoon was free and they could please themselves about how they spent their time.

'We intend to do some walking in the woods above the town,' Edith and Anne told Felicity. 'You can join us if you like.'

'I'll let you know. I expect to be pretty busy seeing that my arrangements are all working smoothly for the rest of the tour. But thank you all the same. I'll remember your offer. Take care when you go walking, won't you? Don't forget you're in bear country.'

'We know it. We picked up a leaflet at the tourist office, and the things it tells you! Bears object to scent and hairspray—it makes them wild. Very fussy creatures, if you ask me.'

'Take a whistle with you—they object to noise too. I guess you'll be quite safe so near to town. The only trouble is they do like to raid the garbage cans.'

'Yes, we saw they were all fastened high from the ground in the picnic places, but even so some of them had been turned over.'

'People are inclined to be careless about bears,' Felicity explained. 'They think of them as large cuddly objects and don't realise the danger. They'd never treat a lion like that.'

'Don't worry, we'll be careful. We don't intend to go far,' they assured her.

Felicity did not think she had much to worry about with Edith and Anne. They were so sensible and could look after themselves. Reluctantly she realised that she could not help having to contact Trent about future arrangements. What would he be doing this afternoon? She felt almost sure that he would have arranged something with Crystal, but, very much to her surprise, while she was doing some paperwork at the small desk in the window of her room, which faced on to the front of the hotel, she saw Olaf arriving with a car, that presumably he had hired, and Crystal and Denise came out of the hotel to join him.

Shortly after this, she glanced up from her work and gasped in astonishment. Trent came into the driveway with a car that was towing a small motor launch with a cabin, and stopped in the courtyard below. Had he expected Crystal to join him? If so, he was to be disappointed. Minutes later there was a knock on her door, and in response to her 'Come in' Trent entered, wearing a cream safari suit.

'Come along, Felicity, there'll be time enough for making arrangements later. I've hired a car and a boat. I thought you were due for some time off. How about it?'

'But, Trent . . .'

'It's no use refusing,' he told her. 'You can't tell me you're going out with Olaf, because I've just seen him driving off with Crystal and Denise. Come along now, I'll show you something of the country, and we'll end up at Maligne Lake. That's the place to go if you want to see mountains and glaciers.'

Felicity wondered whether he had intended this surprise for Crystal and it had backfired when he saw her with Olaf, so now he had decided to take her. If this was so, she could hardly ask him and therefore would never know. Did she want to go with him? Oh, yes, that foolish Felicity, who was so opposed to all common sense, told her. I don't trust him at all, and yet I'm longing to spend the day with him away from the others, away from all the hustle and worry of the tour.

'I can be ready in fifteen minutes,' she told him.

As she changed into her blue jeans and the sun-top that he said was alluring, she wondered at herself. What nonsense this was! She felt utterly thrilled that she was to spend the day with Trent. I don't even like him, she thought, and remembered that she had told herself this so very often. With a sudden shock of realisation, she thought, it's true, I don't like him but I love him. This feeling I have for him is more than liking. It's love, more love than I have ever felt for any man before. It's not just physical attraction. It's the whole thing. I've gone overboard for someone I can never have, someone who regards me as a kind of joke, something to amuse him while he takes two weeks' relaxation from his serious business of living, someone who would like to make love to me but doesn't believe in marriage.

'You're very quiet,' said Trent, as they drove away from the hotel heading for the highway.

'I'm thinking,' said Felicity.

'How about communicating some of those thoughts, then?'

Oh no, thought Felicity. She was astonished and confused by the direction in which her thoughts were leading. Could this sudden idea be true? Cautiously she took it out and began to examine it all round. Don't be ridiculous, she said to herself. You can't love Trent. It's completely ill-advised and idiotic. But then, without turning his head, he took his hand from the wheel and enclosed her own in his, giving it a brief squeeze before returning it.

'Well?' he asked.

She looked at his side view, the rather stern profile, softened by the long silky lashes beneath the heavy brows, the strong neck and glimpse of bronzed chest muscles beneath the pale safari jacket, and her heart gave a deep throb and then continued with hastened beat. How foolish I am, she thought.

'Do you really want to know what I'm thinking?' she asked.

'Very much. I'm curious to know how that mind works inside the lovely body.'

'I'm wishing I'd missed that plane at Dorval,' she told him.

'But you did miss your plane.'

'Of course, but then I came with you. Perhaps it would have been better if I'd let Wyatt have his way.'

'Wyatt? Are you missing him, then, Felicity?'

'Hardly. I phoned him to let him know my postal address, but since then I haven't heard from him at all. No, Wyatt was a very small incident in my life.'

'Are you regretting coming here? Isn't the job turning out as wonderful and glamorous as you expected?'

'I didn't think it would be particularly glamorous,' she said. 'I know what hard work a courier's job is. However, it hasn't gone smoothly, not as smoothly as I would have wished.'

'I shouldn't worry,' he shrugged. 'Everyone seems happy.'

No, you wouldn't worry, of course, Trent, she thought. What I really regret is just the fact that I ever met you at all. Some day maybe I'll tell you that, but not today. No, I'll enjoy today, just being with you, for there's not much time left. In a few days the tour will be over for both of us and your

whim of becoming a coach driver for two weeks will
be finished. But what about me? Every time I take
visitors on this route, I shan't be able to help myself
remembering you. That's what I mean when I say I
wish I'd never met you. There'll be too much to
remember.

So why are you consenting to spend the day with
him? asked that sensible self. Oh, foolish Felicity,
you run the risk of having much more to remember,
don't you? But she put all these warnings aside. I
must have this time with him, she thought.

They had left the wider country around Jasper
and were now on a rougher, narrower road, with
great slopes of shaley mountains to the side. Presently
they came to a lake and Trent halted so they could
have a good view of it. They got out of the car and
walked to where they could overlook it, and Trent
put his arm around her bare shoulders, so casually
that she could not object, but she was far too conscious of that brown hand upon her warm upper arm
and of the quivering thrill that had flashed through
her body at this small, insignificant caress.

'Medicine Lake,' said Trent. 'It's like a leaky
bathtub. In summer, as you see it here, it's normal,
fed by melting glacier ice and snow, but in fall and
winter it disappears, flowing out of the bathtub, and
leaves just rubble and boulders. The river flows
through a system of underground caves and pas-
sages and rises to the surface again in Maligne Canyon, sixteen kilometres down the valley. The Indians
thought its strange disappearance was some kind of
magic, so they called it Bad Medicine. It's a very odd
business. They've used special dyes to trace the water
from the lake to its outlets, but they haven't located
the entrance to the system. It's been suggested that
there may be one of the largest cave systems anywhere in the world underneath here, but so far it's

inaccessible and it will probably remain so.'

Although the day was warm, Felicity shuddered.

'What a horrible thought! All those dark water-ways underneath the surface.'

'Caverns measureless to man,' said Trent. 'It does present rather a challenge, doesn't it?'

'Not to me,' said Felicity.

'Nor me neither,' said Trent. 'I like my challenges to be in the open, not under the ground.'

'But don't you have mining interests?'

'Ah, yes, but I can pay other people to do it for me.'

'But maybe they don't like going under the ground either.'

'If they don't like it, they needn't do it, need they? That's one thing I've learned in life, Felicity, you don't ever have to do anything you don't really want to. Remember that.'

'I will remember, Trent.'

'How arrogant he is, thought Felicity. How can I love him so?

Soon they reached Maligne Lake, the colour of aquamarine, lying so peacefully still in its amphi-theatre of mountains.

'It doesn't look very malign,' said Felicity.

'Certainly it appears placid enough, but there's plenty of reason for its name, believe me. The thunder of avalanches can be heard any time of the year at the south end, and it's fed by seven glaciers, so it isn't a very bright idea to bathe here.'

'The water looks glorious, sparkling sapphire and then turquoise, but very, very cold even today,' said Felicity.

'That's glacial water coloured by fine silt, par-ticles of dust trapped in the form of crystals.'

'It's an astonishing colour, almost unreal.'

Although there did not appear to be much private boating here, only large launches for tourists, Trent soon arranged with the authorities that he could take his borrowed boat around the lake. He seems to have a very persuasive nature, thought Felicity.

'Do you always get your own way?' she asked, as she stepped into the boat.

'Almost always,' he grinned. 'I can think of one or two occasions when I haven't, Felicity, and I think you were there at the time.'

With difficulty she met the cool emerald gold gaze of his eyes upon her.

'However,' he continued, 'possibly it's good for my morale to be checked on occasion. I've always enjoyed a challenge.'

'Yes,' Felicity agreed. 'It's not good for you or anyone always to get whatever it is they desire.'

'I'm quite happy to mark time, if that's what you want, but I usually get what I desire in the end. I'm a patient man, Felicity, but be warned.'

'Patient?' she laughed. 'I would never have put that as one of your virtues.'

The boat started easily and soon they were chugging smoothly over the sapphire lake. Felicity put on her fluffy sweater again, for the wind over the water was chilly. The boat was small and the seat beside the wheel scarcely big enough for two people. Trent steered with one hand, his other arm along the back of the seat. There was no other alternative than to sit very close to him, and Felicity realised that she did not mind this. You're very far gone in love, she told herself, when just the fact of sitting here, the cool wind in your face and the warmth of his body counteracting that, can make you feel this sense of suffocating joy. All around them the mountains arose, lifting incredibly high, snowy peaks towards the blue sky.

'Those glaciers have been there for centuries, and they'll still be there when we've gone. It makes me feel very small,' Felicity told Trent.

'Don't think of it. We still have plenty of living to do.'

'Did you know,' he added, 'that a woman was one of the first to explore this part of the country? Mary Schaffer, a wealthy Quaker from Pennsylvania. The Indians called her Yahe-Weha, the mountain woman. An Indian, Samson Beaver, had drawn a rough map for her describing a legendary lake. She was determined to find it, so she set out with a packtrain and became the first woman to see Maligne Lake in 1908. She explored the lake on a small raft held together with only wooden pegs and thongs. She must have been able to see these icy blue waters through the large cracks in the bottom. As she came through the narrows into the expanse of the lake, she said there burst upon her the finest view in the Rockies.'

Felicity felt a throb of sympathy with this Mary Schaffer who had lived so long ago. The lake and mountains lay before them, the whole of it unspoiled, just as it must have been on that day when it was first seen, a gem of sapphire, surrounded by a backdrop of high mountains and glaciers, hanging above in the snowy wastes like vast angels' wings.

They skimmed across the lake, seemingly the only people in the blue expanse, the only people in the world, it seemed to Felicity. The splash of water, the steady throb of the engine, seemed to echo in the wilderness, the only sounds to be heard in all this solitude.

'That's Spirit Island,' said Trent, pointing to a wooded clump of land. 'Sometimes it's joined to the land by a narrow peninsula. When this happens and one can walk across, the Indians say it will be a good year for fishing.'

'Are there fish in this cold water?' Felicity asked.

'Not naturally, but they've stocked it from 1928

with brook and rainbow trout. I've brought a fishing rod, just in case. How do you fancy a meal of trout fresh from the lake?'

Trent brought the boat to a standstill, deftly pulling it into the bank where there was an inlet with woodland almost down to the edge of the lake. It was perfectly lovely, peaceful wooded country with the lake in front of them and the mountains towering all around.

'Oh, do look, what's that?' cried Felicity.

She could hardly believe her eyes. A group of moose were wading in the shallows, their beautiful antlers held high above the water as they moved slowly along.

'They don't seem to feel the cold,' she said.

'I guess they're used to it. You even find caribou here about two thousand feet up where the forest thins out and you get a kind of alpine tundra. It's a very harsh life up there, with high winds and cold temperatures, but they manage to survive on a diet of lichen, coming down lower to feed near the lake in the winter. It's a true wilderness area where you can find caribou. They don't linger in a place where there are people.'

'And bears?'

'Oh, of course, there are bears around. The grizzly, the one with the hump on his back, is the most dangerous. But there are brown ones as well—*Ursus Horribilis*. But if they start increasing too much around the lake, they're darted and taken farther up the mountains. Now, enough of lessons for one day. What say you get out our picnic and we have our long-awaited lunch?'

He seemed to have thought of everything. As Felicity unpacked the perfectly prepared food, she could not help wondering again whether it had really been meant for Crystal and somehow his surprise

had backfired because Olaf had taken Crystal and
Denise out. But she tried to put such thoughts aside
and live just for the moment, and the moment was
wonderful. She was alone with Trent as she had
longed to be, in utter solitude, the only living things
those moose silhouetted darkly against the blue
sapphire of the lake, and a few birds that skimmed
effortlessly above the waters.

They sat on a rug and ate delicious cold meats,
tiny bread rolls, various salads, and with this they
drank a sparkling wine that had chilled instantly
when Trent suspended it into the lake. Felicity
forgot her usual caution and did not even notice
as Trent filled her glass again. Let me be happy just
for today, she thought. Trent was at his charming
best, talking to her, smiling, not a trace of arrogance
in his manner. Take care, a small voice warned her.
However charming he is, you mustn't let him know
how you feel. But she felt so happy, so relaxed in his
company today. It can't go on, the warning voice
continued. This is only for today and you want it to
last for a lifetime.

He made to fill her glass again, but this time she
was wary and brought her hand over it.

'No more, Trent, but that was all delicious. I'll
start clearing things away, shall I? Just in case *Ursus
Horribilis* is in the vicinity.'

'Ah, no, Felicity, don't be so conscientious. Come
over here to me.'

He was sitting a few yards away, his back against
a tree, and now he held out his arms to her in invitation. His emerald green eyes had an almost
hypnotic power. Knowing she was acting against
her better judgment, she slowly walked the few
paces and kneeled down at his side. One of his hands
came out and slowly he stroked the outline of her
face, brushing back the tendrils of red-gold hair that

had blown over her brow.

'Lovely Felicity, how do you feel about me now? Better, worse, just the same?'

The touch of that brown hand was agony. She felt dizzy with the desire to be in his arms, to feel his kisses, his mouth hard and sure on her own. All around her was the hot fragrance of wild grasses and she thought she would always remember this, together with the cold snow water smell of the lake itself.

'Just the same,' she told him.

It's true, she thought, he has always had the power to thrill me, to make me long for some rapture that only he can give.

'My staid Felicity,' he said, 'I've practically kidnapped you to bring you to this glorious place and all you can say is "Just the same". With you, I don't win, do I?'

'Let's walk,' she said. 'Those woods look so inviting.'

Anything to get away from the temptation to respond to that hand's caresses.

'If that's what you want. This is your day, Felicity. You may do as you please, but I had rather hoped what you wish might please me too. However, if walk we must, let's go.'

Away from the lake, the day was warm now and Felicity had discarded her sweater in favour of the suntop that showed her bare brown arms and shoulders. Trent too had taken off his jacket and his chest showed bronze above the taut waist of his narrow cream slacks. Sun dappled the path as they wandered beneath the trees upon the soft bed of pine needles. Trent's arm was around her bare shoulders, softly caressing the smooth silkiness of her upper arm, and Felicity felt an overwhelming desire to halt and turn her face to be kissed, to give way to her innermost feelings upon this one lovely day. I may never be alone with him again, she thought.

A deer, dappled brown and gold like the sunlit forest, sprang out of their path ahead of them, and as quickly disappeared. They had stopped walking, standing quite still as the beautiful animal froze, panic-stricken, great brown eyes startled, before it raced for the thicket.

'Oh, wasn't that glorious?' Felicity exclaimed, breathless with excitement.

Trent turned to her, tilted her chin, and she felt the rough texture of his jaw before she was overwhelmed by the savage intensity of his kiss.

'Glorious,' he said as he released her. 'A good description.'

'I was talking about the deer,' Felicity protested.

'Oh, so was I. What else could be glorious around here?'

She felt he was mocking her. His green-gold eyes were sparkling, his mobile mouth, that had just reluctantly released hers, was now curved in a smile.

'You make fun of me all the time,' she accused him.

'If I took everything you say seriously, I'd never get any kisses. You're such a cool customer, Felicity. It's a great temptation to shatter that calm—and, confess it, I've done so on occasion, haven't I?'

'Wishful thinking,' vowed Felicity.

She must never let this infuriating man know how she really felt, she told herself. If he only knew how difficult she found it to resist his wild lovemaking, she would be lost.

They wandered on and soon came to a sunlit glade. Wild roses rioted in the surrounding bushes and in the grass grew fireweed and the thrusting red flowers of the Indian paintbrush.

'Just the place for our afternoon rest,' said Trent.

Felicity looked at him suspiciously, but she consented to sit upon the soft ground cushioned with the needles from pines and larches. Somewhere in the woods came the sound of water tumbling over rocks, and a bird sang sweetly, its notes falling into the air like echoing crystal. They sat for a long time, listening to the silence, hardly speaking.

'We seem to be the only people to be left alone in the world,' said Felicity.

'Let's imagine we are,' said Trent. 'Forget everything else, Felicity. Our heaven could be here.'

She felt a shuddering sensation of panic as his hand loosened the narrow strap of her dress, and his mouth came down to wander over her bare shoulders, and sought the hollow that lay between her breasts. The fragrance of the forest was all around her as he gently pushed her down and found her mouth with his. Her hands came up to smooth the flat planes of his chest where the muscles rippled underneath the silky bronze of his skin. His body in its hard maleness was like that of a lithe spirited animal, she thought, one which was proud of its own strength. And at that she checked. It was true. His feeling for her was merely animal desire, no more. He had never pretended anything else. Her hands left the silky, golden shoulders.

'No, Trent, I can't.'

His head came down to her breast and she felt the rough curls against her bare flesh.

'Sweet Felicity, how can you refuse us this glorious afternoon? Once in a lifetime you're offered a perfect experience, and this is it. We may never again be in this lovely wilderness together with the opportunity to make love, and nothing and nobody here besides ourselves. Forget this stupid pride of yours and surrender yourself to me. You'll never regret it, I promise you.'

There was so much burning ardour in the golden blaze of his eyes that she could not meet his gaze but turned away. Her hands were shaking as she replaced the strap of her dress, for she knew that if she looked at him, she would once again be in his arms. And this time there would be no turning back.

'No, Trent, I won't be seduced by you just to give you a small gratification to your own ego. You're pleased enough with yourself already without having me as another conquest to hang on your belt.'

She could look at him now and that flame, that had seemed to pulsate in the flashing golden depths of his eyes, flickered and died. She had a feeling as if she had killed some living, breathing creature. But how could that be? She must guard against being sentimental, because certainly his feelings for her were nothing but a desire for the pleasure of the moment to be as quickly forgotten when he returned to his own world.

'I should have known,' he said. 'I should have been warned by your former reactions to me, but how should I know that, in spite of the warm gold of your hair, the curves of that lovely body, the passionate surrender of those soft, gentle lips, inside there's a heart cold as that green snow water?'

Oh, Trent, she thought, if only you knew! His words were like hailstones, battering against her resistance, but she willed herself to be firm in her resolve.

'I'm not your kind, Trent. If being cold means not wanting to have a swift passionate affair that means basically nothing, then I am cold. If ever I fall in love, I'll want it to last for a lifetime, and you've said yourself that's not for you. Making love because the day is fine, the scenery glorious, isn't my idea of romance. You only want me because the perfect opportunity is there, but by next week we'll have gone our separate ways and you'll have forgotten me.'

Trent laughed but there was little humour in the sound.

'My poor Felicity, how can I convince you that we could have had something wonderful to remember each other by?'

'I don't want to remember you, Trent. I never asked for your company, and I would rather forget you.'

'I didn't realise that you disliked me so much,' he shrugged.

'Well, now you know.'

Better for him to think this than that he should know the truth, she thought.

As they walked back to the lake, the sun, that had been sending shafts between the trees, had disappeared, and the woods, which had appeared so beautiful just a short time ago, seemed to Felicity to be as gloomy as her own mood. Her heart was filled with sickening pain. I love him, she thought, and yet if I were to surrender myself to him for so brief a time, I would be storing up heartbreak for a lifetime. She was so miserable that she hardly noticed that they had reached the edge of the woods, until Trent put his hand out to stop her, as they reached the outermost rim of the trees.

'Wait,' he said in a low voice. 'Stand dead still.'

She froze, for at the water's edge, where they had left the boat, she could see a strange, dark shape. She had never before seen a live bear, and yet she realised that this was exactly as she had always imagined one, large, shaggy, brown and shambling. It was investigating the contents of the boat with clumsy paws, throwing aside the flasks and cutlery to get at the remains of their picnic, then it stood there eating a cream pastry, looking rather ludicrous with cream and jam all over its nose. It looked so like some humorous circus turn that Felicity lost some of her freezing fear, but only for a moment.

'What should we do?' she whispered.

'Stay here and hope he'll go. We're down wind of him, let's hope he won't get our scent. He's only a young brown bear, fortunately, not a grizzly.'

Trent drew her back behind a bush and they peered out at the animal, who was making short work of whatever he could find to eat in the boat. But he still wasn't satisfied. Suddenly he gave a low growl and started to claw at the boat, ripping at the paintwork, evidently hoping to find some more to eat.

'This won't do,' said Trent. 'You stay here—and for God's sake keep quiet.'

'Oh, Trent, no, don't do it!'

But he had seized a branch from the ground and was advancing on the animal, who, still grunting and tearing, was unaware of his presence. However, Trent gave a great shout as he came nearer and the bear turned. To Felicity, standing there, feeling as if she had turned to stone, this was the most terrifying moment of her life. Trent had said this was a young bear, but as he reared to his feet, standing on his hind legs, he seemed to her to tower above Trent, in spite of the man's six-foot height.

Trent waved the branch around his head, uttering strange yells, and it seemed to Felicity as if they had momentarily been translated back in years to that time when the Indians lived here and had to defend their lives against the creatures of the wilderness. Trent, with his bare bronzed frame and his dark hair and profile of an eagle, thrusting his frail weapon at the growling bear, seemed like a wild, primitive man of the forest. The bear lifted one great paw as if to strike out at the small stick and it seemed to Felicity as if it must surely rip Trent with those mighty claws. Although he had told her to be quiet, now a piercing scream came from her lips and she was not even aware that it was she herself who was making this noise. But the bear had heard it. He wavered in his approach to Trent, dropped to his four feet and shambled off into the forest, pulling in his rear quarters like some whipped cur.

Trent dropped the stick and came towards her. The reaction from extreme fear to relief was tremendous. Tears rained down her face and she put her arms around his neck, feeling the vitality of him flowing back towards her, giving her strength.

'It's all right,' she heard him murmur against her wet cheek. 'He's gone, Felicity, I don't think he'll bother us any more. He was just curious and greedy. Bears are.'

'I . . . I thought he was going to kill you!'

'Well, he was just about to take a mighty swipe at me, certainly, but that hideous yelling of yours saved me. Wherever did that noise come from? This little throat doesn't seem capable of producing such a sound.'

The long fingers briefly caressed her neck, then wiped away her tears, but, when his lips seemed near, Felicity hastily dropped her hands from their clinging embrace of him. His smile was rather ironic. What other man, she wondered, could be so imperturbable when he had just had a close encounter with a bear?

'For someone who dislikes me so strenuously, you seemed rather alarmed at my impending demise,' observed Trent.

She laughed shakily.

'It would have been awkward to have you dead at my feet. Besides, I can't drive a boat.'

If you can joke about it, so can I, she thought. But oh, Trent, if you knew how I really feel, and how hard it is to disguise it!

His arms fell to his sides.

'Speaking of driving the boat, we'd better have a look if that wretched animal has done any harm to it.'

Felicity was too concerned with the scratch marks to see anything else, but Trent almost immediately noticed something much more serious.

'He's punctured our fuel tank,' he said. 'Look at this.'

A small patch of oily substance was casting a rainbow patch upon the blue water.

'Is it bad?' asked Felicity.

Trent shrugged.

'Bad enough. We'd better get going straight away. The tank's pretty full. If it's leaking slowly, we may just be able to make it.'

Without stopping even to put on their outer garments, they got into the boat and started off.

'What if the fuel doesn't last out?' asked Felicity.

She was pressed up against Trent in the narrow cockpit, even now painfully aware of the feel of his golden skin against her own bare shoulders.

'We'll meet that problem when we get to it,' said Trent.

For once his mouth was serious, drawn in a straight line.

But the moment was sooner than he had anticipated. As they were drawing close to one of the small islands upon the lake, the engine spluttered and died. The sun was low now. Felicity had not noticed how evening was drawing in.

'Fortunately we have a paddle,' said Trent. 'Looks like we have no choice but to spend the night here.'

Felicity's heart seemed to drop to her feet.

'But we have to get back! What about the tour? We're due to make an early start tomorrow. We have to get right through to Banff, taking in Lake Louise.'

'Nothing we can do, I'm afraid. It won't hurt for them to make a later start. It's likely someone will miss us soon from the boathouse, but it's late for them to start searching in the dark. No, there's nothing for it but to steer to the island. One thing's certain—there won't be any bears there and there's a comfortable bed in the cabin, so you needn't worry.'

Not worry at the prospect of spending the night shut up in that tiny cabin with Trent? Everything I touch on this trip seems to turn into a nightmare, thought Felicity. What had happened to the sweet content she had experienced earlier in the day?

They landed at the small wooded island where there was even a jetty to tie up the boat. The view from here was one of the most wonderful she had seen so far, but Felicity could only give a fleeting thought to it. Trent helped her out of the boat and they stood on the jetty gazing over the water. A fish jumped out of the water and landed with a splash. Trent put his arm around her shoulders and gave her a little shake.

'Stop panicking, Felicity, and begin to enjoy yourself. We may even be able to catch some trout for our supper. The bear has effectively put paid to anything we had left to eat.'

The sun was going down, casting rosy shadows over the snowfields and the water had turned from turquoise to a deep sapphire. Trent fetched a rod from the boat and at the same time brought her fluffy sweater and slipped it over her head. As he did so, he kissed the top of her shoulders.

'Pity to cover you,' he said, 'but the wind is cold from the water.'

He too had put on his jacket and now he baited the rod and cast into the shadowed water. Almost immediately he was rewarded with a bite and landed a small trout, and, in a little while, he had four.

'They bite well at this time of day,' he said. 'Now for a fire to cook them by.

'A good thing bears don't drink wine,' he said some time later. 'We were fortunate it was in the cabin and he didn't reach it to smash it up.'

They had retrieved some paper plates and some forks and the taste of the trout, cooked over wood coals, was delicious.

'Think how much our passengers are paying in Jasper for just such a meal,' said Trent.

'I don't want to think of my passengers at all,' said Felicity. 'There's going to be hell to pay if we don't arrive in time tomorrow.'

Trent only looked amused.

'You must indeed be agitated, my proper Felicity, to be using such strong language! Don't worry, we'll get there eventually. No problem. Your passengers will have to wait—do them good. They've been cossetted enough so far.'

But they haven't, thought Felicity. So many things have gone wrong this trip. And oh, Trent, if you'd never come, I wouldn't be here in this predicament.

They sat beside the glowing embers for a long time, mostly in silence. In spite of her nervousness, when they had eaten the trout and had a glass of wine, Felicity felt a kind of happiness creeping up on her.

'How many times did you want to be on a desert island when you were a child? Well, this is it, Felicity.'

But I'm not a child, she thought.

'We'd better turn in,' said Trent eventually. 'If the worst comes to the worst, I'll have to use the paddle to get us back, so we'll have to start at first light.'

There was only one bunk, a kind of wide seat in the little cabin, but they found a couple of blankets in a cupboard.

'I'll take one and you can have the other.'

'But where are you going to sleep?' asked Felicity.

'Beside the fire—where else? You made it completely clear to me, when we were on the boat, that you'd rather face death and destruction than have me anywhere around.'

'Oh, Trent, you'll be too cold. I . . . I don't mind if you sleep here, provided . . .'

'Provided I don't make love to you, is that it? How many times must I tell you, Felicity, that I've never yet made love to an unwilling woman?'

I don't suppose you have, thought Felicity. I guess all of them have been far too willing, just like me. But you'll never know, of that I'm determined.

'However, I prefer the cold outdoors to the temptation of sleeping beside you,' Trent went on. 'My virtuous intentions might be too stretched. Lie down on the bunk and I'll tuck you into the blanket,' he ordered.

She did as she was told and he rolled the blanket around her until only her face was showing. 'Sleep well,' he said. She felt a soft kiss on her mouth and then he was gone. Through the window of the cabin she could see him, a dark shape beside the dying embers of the fire. She saw him put on some more wood and the flames leapt up. In the orange light, his features looked dark, like one of those Indians who had lived here long ago. The night was full of stars and she recalled that other time when he had tucked a blanket around her and she had watched the universe whirl by from his jet plane. It seemed light years away, and yet it was scarcely two weeks. In a few days he would have gone back and she would never see him again. Can I ever forget him? she asked herself. Will it be like he says and I'll regret that we never made love together?

For a long time she lay awake watching Trent as he sat immobile, gazing into the glowing flame. What was he thinking of, sitting there so still? He seemed to her mysterious, rather frightening, far removed from the man who teased and made fun of her by day. The water made regular lapping sounds against the boat, and gradually, to this sound, she was lulled to sleep.

Suddenly she was wide awake again. What time was it? She looked at the illuminated dial of her watch. Three o'clock. She sat up and looked out. Trent still sat there and the fire was still alight. He was wrapped in his blanket, but why wasn't he sleeping? And what had wakened her? Sleepily she recalled her dream. She had been walking in a place somewhat like the Butchart Gardens, but there was no one there but herself and Trent. This is Paradise, she thought. They were lying on a flowery bank high above a vast stretch of blue water, and he was kissing her, embracing her, but this time there was no holding back. There was a rapture here that she had never known before, utter surrender. And then he was gone. He had vanished away and she was alone. She felt such desolation that she cried out, and this was what had wakened her.

Trent was standing up now. He was coming towards the boat.

'Felicity,' he called softly. 'Are you all right?'

'Yes, I think so,' she said. 'I've just wakened. I had a dream.'

'I thought I heard you call. Sure you're all right? Not scared?'

'No, but I won't sleep again. Haven't you had any sleep?'

'Not much. It's damned cold out there, even with the fire.'

'It's not very warm here,' she said.

He came towards her and she felt herself beginning to tremble.

'Oh, Felicity, lovely one, let me keep you warm.'

He lay beside her and drew the blanket around

them. She nestled against him, feeling the warmth of his virile body restoring her own vitality. It was as if she were still in her dream. Whatever I do, I'm going to lose him, she thought. Why not? Why not have his love, or pretence of love, just for one time? She felt she could not bear to sacrifice the memory of that rapture she had felt in the dream. But, with his warm body beside her, she had forgotten about the dark desolation that had followed.

'Trent,' she murmured softly, reaching up her arms to embrace him, seeking his lips that responded with sudden fire.

'And what's happened to the ice-cool Felicity now?' he asked between kisses.

She did not answer, but only knew that she was being borne along on a tide of emotions that she could hardly endure, and yet she dared not deny them. She was in a maze of enchantment, and the reality was more rapturous than the dream.

But suddenly the joy she felt was savagely inter-rupted, as Trent tore his lips from hers and jerked to a sitting position, listening intently.

'Hell and damnation!' he exclaimed.

Now she heard it too, the sound of an engine, from a motor launch, travelling swiftly over the water. In a few seconds Trent was out of the cabin, flourishing a light, and hailing the crew.

'What's the trouble? We missed you but couldn't do much about it until first light,' she heard a mas-culine voice shout out.

First light? Yes, Felicity realised that the dawn was breaking with a paler colour of grey over the pewter-coloured water and the sun was turning the snowy peaks to rose. As she tried to gather herself together, she heard Trent explaining their predicament.

'Too bad, but we can give you a tow,' she heard the ranger say.

Trent came into the cabin looking very matter-of-fact and normal. How could he look like that when she still felt so shattered by the events of the last few minutes? And yet there was something twisted about his smile.

'You're to get your wish,' he said. 'The tour will start on time this morning, and really, Felicity, that's all that matters to you, isn't it?'

CHAPTER ELEVEN

FELICITY had hoped no one need know about their misadventure, but it was not to be. As they arrived at the hotel, Denise and Olaf emerged from the door. Denise was wearing bright red culottes and a strip of red and white striped material across her breasts. Her golden hair stood out on either side of her face in small rippling waves. The colour of Olaf's safari suit emphasised the vivid blue of his eyes. They were talking and laughing together, looking very pleased with themselves, but when they saw Felicity and Trent arriving with the damaged boat in tow, they came towards them, staring curiously.

'Hi there,' said Denise. 'Have you been out all night? You sure do believe in making the most of your free time, don't you?'

'We had a slight encounter with a bear,' Trent explained.

'No kidding?'

They examined the clawmarks upon the paintwork of the boat and insisted on hearing the whole story. Felicity realised that it would be all around the party in the next hour and she was right. She had no sooner had her shower and ordered a quick breakfast in her

room than there was a knock at the door and Crystal
swept in.

She looked very elegant today in tobacco brown
slacks suit and tunic of heavy Indian silk. In her
towelling robe, her hair screwed up into a bun, an
untidy knot on top of her head, Felicity felt distinctly at a disadvantage. Those violet eyes scanned
her from head to foot and didn't seem to approve of
what they saw.

'Miss Tait, is it usual for both driver and courier
to spend the night away from the place where your
passengers are staying?'

'No, Mrs Harcourt, it is not, but circumstances
made it impossible for Trent and me to get back to
the hotel.'

The beautiful mouth curled in an unbelieving
sneer.

'How about that, then? Your passengers were looking for you last night wanting information about
restaurants and so on, but you were nowhere to be
found. Really, Miss Tait, your conduct during the
whole of this tour has left a lot missing.'

'I'm sorry you've felt like that, Mrs Harcourt, but
I've had no complaints from anyone else,' said
Felicity firmly. 'In fact, they seem to me to be an
unusually happy party.'

It's only I myself who have been unhappy, she
thought.

'You may think so, but I certainly don't. I suppose
these days one can't expect much of the morals of a
young woman of your type, but I do feel you should
keep your little adventures to your own time and not
let it interfere with your passengers' comfort.'

'I assure you, Mrs Harcourt, there's nothing wrong
with my morals,' said Felicity icily.

'No? And yet you manoeuvred Trent into taking
you away and staying out for the whole night. He's

an attractive man, and after all, he's only human. If a girl throws herself at his head as you seem to have done, one can hardly blame him for making the most of his opportunities.'

'Mrs Harcourt, I hardly think anyone could make Trent do anything he doesn't want to. Surely you of all people should know that.'

'What are you implying?' snapped Crystal. 'I certainly have no personal interest in your squalid little affairs, Miss Tait. Trent's a lot of fun. It didn't hurt to have him spend an evening with me. I'm only sorry that he should be involved with someone like you. All through this tour you've acted as if you created him personally. He's been fortunate to get any time to himself, but don't think for a moment that he really goes for your clinging ways. He hasn't got a very great opinion of you. You should hear him on the subject—or, on the other hand, perhaps you should not.'

'Trent can think what he pleases of me,' said Felicity wearily.

Had Trent really discussed her with Crystal? She felt a swift stab of pain at the thought that this might be so.

'My ex-husband suggested I should bring Denise on this tour because it's usually so reliable and well run. I can't say I think he was right. He'll be most disappointed when I tell him what a mistake he made.'

And with that, Crystal swept out.

When the passengers arrived to board the coach, they were all keen to know the story of the bear and there was a certain amount of teasing about Trent and Felicity having had to stay out during the night. At this Crystal looked furious.

Today the drive through the Jasper and Banff National Parks was to take them through some of the finest mountain scenery in the world, and they were to visit the Columbia ice-field and have a drive over a glacier. The journey was leisurely so that the tourists could take in all the wonderful sights, and, apart from answering questions about the names of mountains, for the most part Felicity was free to study her thoughts. And these were not comfortable. Why did she feel this sense of vain regret? She must forget it. I'm glad, she told herself, glad we were interrupted. It was a moment of weakness when I thought I could surrender to him. I gave in to temptation, but it won't happen again.

Now Olaf came to sit beside her.

'Felicity, I wish to apologise for my behaviour the other night.'

'Think nothing of it, Olaf. I guess it was partly my fault. Somehow I gave you the wrong impression.'

'I had not realised that you and Trent . . . it was foolish of me. Mrs Harcourt said it was very usual for the courier and driver to have some intimate relationship on these tours.'

'Oh, she did, did she?'

Crystal seemed determined to show her, Felicity, up in the worst possible light. She seemed to have had her knife into her from the start, but if she denied having any relationship with Trent, she might have Olaf to deal with again, so she had better keep quiet. Though now he seemed to be more interested in Denise.

'They are very charming, Mrs Harcourt and her daughter, so worldly wise and sophisticated.'

'Oh, yes, they're certainly that,' Felicity agreed.

'I find Denise very attractive, so wild and free. It is difficult to keep up with her.'

Felicity felt a stab of pity for Olaf presumably trying to recapture some kind of youth with Denise, but the tour would soon be over, and certainly Olaf was old enough to look after himself.

Felicity's seat was not far from the driver's and Trent glanced around once or twice, able to see Olaf sitting near to her but not, she thought, over-hearing the conversation. When they arrived at the Athabasca Glacier, and all got out of the coach, his eyes were cold and he murmured, 'Olaf on the trail again, I see.'

'He's more interested in Denise,' Felicity said, but Trent had turned aside and was speaking to Crystal.

'Too bad we missed our date last night,' he was saying. 'Sorry I couldn't make it.'

'Olaf made a good substitute,' said Crystal.

Her voice was icy. She wasn't the kind of woman to be stood up and tolerate it, thought Felicity. So Trent had intended to dine with her, before the bear had interfered with his plans. Felicity felt humiliated. How could Trent have tried to make love to her and yet be going to meet Crystal that same evening? Even more now she was happy that he had been frustrated.

But now all her concern must be to see that her passengers got their seats on the snowcoaches. These were snowmobiles capable of taking about a dozen people at a time, and soon they were buzzing along on a journey of a few miles over the ice, with Mount Andromeda towering above them.

'A glacier is formed where the winter snowfall is so heavy that summer melting doesn't remove it all,' said the young student who was driving them. 'Twenty to thirty feet of snow falls in the ice-field each year, and as the loose, feathery snow is buried by later falls, it's gradually packed close in spherical grains. Over the years, when the ice becomes thick enough, it starts to move down the valley.'

Felicity found it very strange to get out of the snowcoach and walk upon the glacier, feeling that, below her, there was a depth of ice of at least three hundred metres and all around them the mountains were covered in snow, even in summer. It was very slippery and she saw that Olaf was assisting Denise who, as usual, had gone far ahead to anyone else. Crystal had not even descended from the vehicle. She was sitting there with a rather bored expression on her lovely face. Suddenly Felicity was aware that Trent was beside her.

'Magnificent, isn't it?' he said.

He tucked her arm under his and together they took careful steps over the ice. In spite of her distress at the row with Crystal, she felt a moment of great happiness as he guided her over the glacier.

'You can see the layers of ice here formed by differences in the size and arrangement of the ice crystals.'

'I noticed on the way up that the ice in some places had a fantastic colour of green where the light came through it, almost luminous.'

How beautiful it was! She wished she could stay here alone with Trent and not have to think of Crystal, but some of the passengers were starting to complain of the cold. It was summer and they were not very suitably dressed to spend much time on the ice.

'We'd better start assembling our flock,' said Trent. 'Just look at your friend. Could be he's showing off to impress you.'

Olaf had wandered far away over the ice with Denise.

'I wouldn't say it's me he wants to impress,' said Felicity.

Trent gave a mighty shout and the two truants returned to the main party. They all boarded the snowcoach and were taken back to the tea-room at the terminus. It was odd, thought Felicity, to see the bright yellow vehicles, like small beetles, moving over the vast snowfield.

'If you want to, you can walk to the toe of the glacier,' Felicity told her passengers. 'But do be careful. Do heed the warning signs and don't go any further—there are deep crevasses where the ice has folded. But it's interesting to see how the glacier ends.'

Some of the passengers, including Crystal, decided to stay in the coach.

'You don't have to go, surely, Trent,' Felicity heard Crystal murmur, but to her surprise he came along beside her.

'I'd better keep an eye on the passengers,' she heard him say.

'Oh, yes, please, do watch Denise. Miss Tait seems incapable of controlling her properly.'

Am I her keeper? thought Felicity. Surely if she's with Olaf, he can take care of her. I can't give her my undivided attention as Crystal seems to expect, because I must look after the others as well. Anyhow, Trent is here with me, and to her surprise she felt a sense of reassurance, the same that she had felt when he took her arm upon the slippery ice up there in the middle of the glacier.

Here at the toe, the terrain was much rougher, the ice soiled and not very beautiful, convoluted further up into great twisting folds. Higher up too there appeared to be a jumbled mass of crevasses.

'Don't venture any farther than the notices,' Felicity warned them again.

But there were other tourists there who did not seem to be taking the least notice of the dangers. They were climbing up the ice in most unsuitable shoes, intent on seeing as much as possible and on peering down into these deep slits in the ice.

'Oh, come on, Olaf, it's crummy down here. Let's go farther up. It looks more exciting there.'

Before Felicity had time to protest, they were away, with Denise shinning fleetly over the ice and Olaf trying to keep up with her. Soon they were high on the ice, Denise's bright red culottes and anorak showing up clearly but very far away, like tiny figures in a dream.

'They shouldn't have gone there,' said Felicity worriedly. Crystal had remained in the coach and only a handful of passengers had walked to the toe of the glacier, but now they were gazing up at Olaf and Denise, and she could hear murmurs of disapproval ... 'stupid girl' ... 'she's always in trouble' and so on.

'I'll go after them,' said Trent.

'Oh, do be careful,' Felicity warned.

She watched him edge his way up the ice. His shoes, the light shoes of a driver, were not particularly suitable either for negotiating such rough terrain. There was a sudden shout from above, and to her horror, Felicity realised that now she could only see the red figure of Denise. Olaf had disappeared.

Trent cupped his hands and shouted back, 'Olaf has fallen! Bring me a rope and the first aid kit from the coach.'

There was a tow rope in case of emergency, and Felicity ran all the way back over the space that separated the coach from the rest of the party at the glacier's toe to fetch it.

'Someone has gone over the edge,' she explained to those who had remained in the coach.

Crystal started up.

'Is it Denise?' she asked.

'No, Olaf.'

'Oh, thank God!' said Crystal, and sank back into her seat, taking no more interest in what happened.

Felicity felt wildly annoyed. If it had not been for Denise's encouragement, and the fact that Olaf was trying to keep up with her young, foolish ways, he would never have fallen, she thought.

As she made her way up the glacier to where she could see Trent and Denise standing, she realised even more how unutterably stupid they had been to go there in the first place. For every other step she took, she slipped back. Why hadn't they taken note of her warnings? By now several men from the party had come too and were peering down the crevasse where Olaf was lying.

'How is he?' asked Felicity.

'He's conscious,' said Trent. 'But he's hurt his ankle.'

'Oh, why did this have to happen?' grumbled Denise. 'We were having such a lot of fun, and now this! This whole tour has been such a drag. I wish I'd stayed at home.'

'I wish you had,' said Felicity, who, by now beside herself with worry, felt she could not take any more of Denise's moaning.

There was a point of ice like a stalagmite jagged above the surface, and to this Trent managed to attach the rope.

'Will it hold you?' Felicity asked anxiously.

'It will have to. The men can hold on to it too and take a bit of the weight. They'll have to haul Olaf up when I've slung him to the rope.'

She watched him lower himself over the edge and, with the men, she took the weight of his body as he went slowly, hand over hand, down into the crevasse. The rope slackened and she saw with relief that he had reached the injured man. But they still had to get back. She saw him, in the small cramped space available, examining Olaf, who was doubled up in a peculiar position, and she heard the Scandinavian give a stifled moan.

'He's pretty cold,' Trent shouted. 'We must get

him up quickly. I'll tie him in a sling and signal you when to start heaving.'

Very rapidly he arranged the sling and gave a signal. More men had joined them by now and they were able to take the dead weight of Olaf's body. Gradually they brought him to the surface. He looked blue, his usually ruddy colouring quite disappeared. Someone had gone to headquarters to fetch a stretcher, but meanwhile Felicity wrapped him in blankets she had brought from the coach. He smiled weakly at her.

'Is it very painful?' she asked.

'Not now,' he said. 'It feels rather numb at present.'

She saw him looking around as if searching for someone.

'Denise has gone back to the coach,' she explained.

'Just as well. I wouldn't want her to see me like this.'

But she could have stayed, thought Felicity. She's a heartless little creature, Felicity thought.

She could see some people edging their way up the ice with the stretcher.

'You'll soon be comfortable,' she said.

But what about Trent? she thought.

Her first duty was to Olaf, but her whole heart was there where the men were letting down the rope again to get Trent up to safety. Why did she feel so worried about him? He was not injured like Olaf and he would be up again in a short time. The stretcher bearers were here now and she gladly handed Olaf over to them, then turned back to where the men were still standing at the edge of the crevasse. Something seemed to be keeping them. They were talking together and the concerned expressions on their faces set up in her a feeling of terrible dismay.

'What is it?' she cried, as she came with difficulty towards them.

'The ice must have become soft with all the activity at the edge and a whole lot of loose snow slid into the crevasse. It's partially buried your driver and he's having great difficulty uncovering his legs.'

She peered over the edge and saw that Trent was furiously scooping at the pile of snow surrounding him. He seemed buried almost up to his waist.

'Are you all right, Trent?' she called. 'Can you manage?'

'I guess so, but my hands feel as if they're freezing off. I doubt very much whether I'll be able to tie myself to the rope after this.'

Felicity turned to the men.

'He'll never be able to get up without help now. He's been down too long in freezing conditions, and now this. His hands must be numb after clearing that snow.'

'If anyone else goes down, it had better be someone light,' said one of the men. 'This rope isn't meant for this kind of work. It might not be able to hold a third man after all this strain.'

'I'll go,' said Felicity.

She had known somehow all along that this was what she intended to do.

'Lady, are you sure you know what you're in for?'

'I'll be all right—I'm very strong. Don't let's waste any more time. Get the rope up now.'

They hauled on the rope. Trent was still struggling to free himself, but his movements were slower now and sluggish.

'We're sending someone down to help you,' one of the men called to him.

'Don't tell him it's me,' Felicity implored them.

She was already swinging on the rope, halfway down the chasm, when Trent saw her.

'Felicity, for God's sake go back!' he shouted. 'You crazy girl, what's the use of two of us getting stuck down here?'

But she took no notice of him.

'You must be mad,' he said roughly as she stood with difficulty beside him.

'I didn't expect a welcoming committee,' she said, 'but you could at least be civil.'

And with this she set about clearing the rest of the snow and tied the rope firmly around his waist.

'I'm not leaving you here,' he said.

'You have no choice. Now go quickly or else my hands won't stand up to it either.'

Willing hands pulled Trent upwards and in a few minutes the rope was dangling down again. Although Felicity had held her own with Trent, her strength was nearly spent by this time and she struggled to tie herself to the rope, hoping very much that the knot was strong enough. It was the best she could do with hands as cold as this. They started to pull her up, but she had not got very far when she felt the rope beginning to loosen.

'Stop hauling!' she shouted. 'I'll have to try to tighten the knot.'

It was a terrifying sensation as she swung in midair over the crevasse. The rope had developed a pendulum motion and began to revolve slowly at first and then faster in a dizzying, sickening whirl. Her hands felt like ungainly paws as she tried to fasten the knot tighter, but at last she seemed to make some progress.

'Try it now!' she shouted, and this time, slowly and giddily, she made her way up.

In front of the cheering crowd, Trent enveloped her in a clumsy embrace, his face icy against her own cold cheek.

'It's like being hugged by a polar bear!' she protested.

He let her go and she swayed dizzily.

'Don't ever do anything as mad as that again,' he told her. 'I've never felt so helpless, with you dangling on the end of that flimsy rope and me with hands that were no use whatsoever.'

'How are they now?' Felicity asked.

'Recovering slowly. They feel at the moment as if they've been boiled in oil.'

'And Olaf?'

'He'll live. They've sent for an ambulance. I doubt that his ankle is broken, it seemed merely sprained to me, but we'll have to get him to the hospital for X-rays. We can't take any chances.'

'Poor Olaf,' said Felicity. 'I must go to him straight away.'

Trent's smile that had invigorated her, in spite of her fatigue, vanished now, but Felicity at this moment could only think of her injured passenger.

'I'd better go with Olaf to hospital,' she told Trent. 'I can't leave him to travel in the ambulance alone. I think you'll be able to reassure the others. Will your hands be recovered sufficiently to drive the coach?'

Trent smiled laconically.

'It seems they'll have to be, won't they? Yes, sure, Felicity, I can manage. Save your worry for Olaf, he needs your attention more than I do.'

You're saying you don't need me, aren't you, Trent? she thought. But it isn't that I want to go with Olaf, she longed to say. My only desire is to stay with you. She was still very shaken by the shock of seeing him helpless below the ice. If only you knew how I felt then, she thought. Loving you like this is too horribly painful. Why did it ever start?

CHAPTER TWELVE

As Trent had surmised, Olaf's ankle was badly sprained but not broken and he was able to continue the tour with the aid of a stick and a heavy bandage, but there would be no more pursuing the wandering will-o'-the-wisp that was Denise. Felicity had reported the accident to her firm, but so far had had no response. Maybe they're waiting until I get back, she thought, but accidents can happen in the most well conducted tours, so I hope they won't think too badly of me.

They were staying in Banff for the next few days, making excursions around the area, and she was kept busy arranging these and giving advice to her passengers. They drove around Sundance Canyon, went to lovely Lake Louise, set like a jewel in its ring of mountains, and they enjoyed a sight of the heavy-headed, shaggy buffalo in the paddocks of their reserve, and Olaf was able to bathe in the hot sulphur springs to rejuvenate his injured ankle. All around them was the ageless splendour of the high, snow-clad mountains.

Except for the times when they were together on the excursions, Felicity had tried to avoid Trent. Surrounded by other people, and answering their questions, she felt some degree of safety, but she knew she must beware of being alone with him, for, since their adventure on the lake and the episode of the glacier, she was very much afraid she might betray her true feelings. When they did meet or have any kind of communication, his manner was brusque even to the point of rudeness and she wondered whether the attraction he had felt towards her now was over and done with.

She was surprised therefore when, at breakfast one morning, he came over to her table and said, 'Hi, Felicity, I owe you a date for coming to my rescue so promptly the other day. How about going up Sulphur Mountain this morning?'

'You don't owe me anything,' said Felicity hastily. 'I came down for you because it needed someone light.'

She did not want an outing with him because he felt under some sense of obligation. In fact she did not want any kind of date that would involve being alone with him. But he was adamant, as he usually was when he had made up his mind to something.

'Come along. You've been fussing so over your passengers, you deserve a break. On Sulphur Mountain we'll be high above the world with mountain sheep for chaperones.'

Ah, it was foolish to store up more pain, more memories, she thought, but she could not resist it. This morning she was wearing slacks and jacket of bright denim blue and a white cotton shirt with a small edging of broderie anglaise. She took a scarf from her suitcase and tied it around her neck. It was a particularly beautiful one, blue, the colour of her eyes, with paler blue and yellow butterflies looking as if they were ready to fly from the printed silk. Her hair, newly washed, was as silky as the scarf, standing away from her head, a shining mane of red-gold.

When she came down, Trent had a hired car waiting and drove along Banff Avenue, passing the crowded walkways with their souvenir shops and restaurants, across the bridge over the Bow River, past the park and into Mountain River. Two miles on, past the hot springs, they came to the lower terminal. As it happened there were few tourists waiting and they found themselves alone on a small gondola that soon took off from its base. As the machinery clanked and they swung into the air, Felicity drew in her breath sharply.

'Scared?' asked Trent, and slipped his arm around her shoulders.

Once again she felt reassured. How was it that this man could arouse such mixed feelings in her? He, who had often terrified her, could make her feel safe as well.

'I always have been rather scared of heights,' she admitted.

'You didn't show much sign of it the other day,' he said.

That was because I was more scared of what was happening to you, she thought. I couldn't think of myself in that situation. I love him better than life, she thought. But I have to hide it from him.

Up and up they went, the gondola swinging out over the vast drop of the rugged mountain. Far below them was Banff with its shops and restaurants, but up here, between earth and sky, they were back in the rocky wilderness with only this frail looking craft to guide them up to the top of the mountain. In just eight minutes they had risen over two thousand feet and were at a height of seven thousand five hundred. They disembarked and Felicity found herself swaying rather giddily but glad to be on firm ground again.

'Back in civilisation,' said Trent as they took coffee in the tea-room at the top, overlooking the vast panorama spread before them. 'Even the mountain sheep are tamed.'

For there were several shaggy, horned animals begging for titbits at the door of the place.

'Let's walk,' he said, when they were once again outside, and he led the way on to the path that followed the mountain ridge. There had been so many tourists at the tea-room that somehow Felicity had imagined the whole place crowded, but here, as soon as they were out of sight of the terminal, they were in a different world. The path led along the top between trees that had been racked by mountain winds. One or two mountain sheep stared and then disappeared behind rocks, totally unlike their brothers who had forsaken the wilderness for an easy life at the tea-room.

Going uphill, Felicity was surprised to find herself a little breathless, and was glad of Trent's hand on her arm.

'Take it easy,' he advised. 'We're pretty high, you know.'

'Silly of me. I hadn't realised that it would make a difference to my breathing.'

He turned suddenly towards her, pinning her against a gnarled and windblown tree. His eyes glinted with a kind of humour that she dreaded and she felt he was laughing at her.

'Let's see how kissing feels at this altitude, shall we?'

His mouth was on hers, and, under the thin shirt, she could feel his chest muscles ripple beneath the bronzed skin. At her back was the rough bark of the tree. Was that why she felt herself willingly pressed against the steel-like hardness of his body, suffocatingly aware of the softness of her own?

'Pretty good,' said Trent, releasing her. 'What do you think?'

'It doesn't feel any different to me,' said Felicity, trying to speak calmly.

It was true, she thought. His touch, his kiss never failed to arouse in her a desperate enchantment of the senses, wherever she happened to be.

His eyes, his teasing smile seemed to mock her.

'Ice-cool Felicity, you have your feet very much on the ground, don't you? And yet your lips tell me a different story. At this moment, I'd like to be a brigand and take you away to some nice comfortable cave on the mountains where I could make love to you in peace and to hell with our passengers.'

'Fortunately for me that isn't possible,' said Felicity calmly. 'We have a date with our passengers later this afternoon. I think we'd better turn back now, Trent.'

'As you wish, ice maiden.'

Down again, swinging over the vast space between the mountain top and the terminal at the bottom. This time there were other people in the gondola, and Felicity was glad of it. And yet how lovely it had been to be with Trent alone on the mountain. When she thought of his kisses, a shuddering thrill seemed to invade her body. How soon it will be over? she thought. In a few days he'll be gone and I'll never see him again. By next week he'll have forgotten me, but how can I go on doing this same tour, week after week, remembering him?

They were to leave Banff the following morning and start on the homeward journey, but later during that day, when they came in from their excursion, Felicity was surprised to be told by the hotel manager that a visitor awaited her in her room. Hurrying up there, she found a young woman in the courier uniform of the firm, a girl she vaguely remembered meeting when she had visited the office.

'Oh, hi, nice to see you,' she said.

'Hi, I'm Lucy Hastings. You are Felicity Tait, aren't you?'

She was a slim, rather plain yet well-groomed girl, but at the moment she seemed somehow embarrassed.

'Is there anything I can do for you?' asked

Felicity. 'Are you with another party here?'

Lucy shook her head.

'No. Look, would you like a drink or a cigarette or something?'

'I don't smoke, but we can go out for a drink later if you like,' said Felicity, rather puzzled.

'I . . . I just thought . . . oh well, I guess I'll have to spell it out some time. They've sent me to take your place. Here's the letter.'

Felicity felt as if she had been dropped into the crevasse again but this time without a rope.

'No!' she gasped. 'No, it isn't possible!'

As she read the letter, the print seemed to blur and waver in front of her eyes. She looked at the other girl, who was gazing at her with a very sympathetic expression.

'I don't understand it. They say they've had complaints about my conduct on this tour, and that now, after the accident I reported, they feel I'm not suitable to continue with it. But everyone has seemed so happy. Who could have complained?'

And then, of course, it suddenly came to her.

'Crystal Harcourt! It must be she. I've had nothing but trouble with her since the tour began.'

'You've got it in one,' said Lucy. 'I wasn't supposed to tell you, but now you've guessed. Her ex-husband is one of the directors of the firm, and although they're divorced, I understand they're still buddies. He'd like to get her back, so anything she says goes. Too bad you seem to have got on the wrong side of her—not that that's difficult, by all accounts. And that daughter of hers is pretty pushy too. You were unlucky to get the pair of them on your first trip, but that's it. They've sent a new driver too,' Lucy added.

'A new driver?'

'Yes, the one you should have had in the first place

was free to come now, so they asked him to finish off this tour, so he could get back to his wife and wouldn't have much time away. The other driver was only a temp, wasn't he? I've brought both your cheques to pay you off. They've included your air fare back to Vancouver.'

'A new driver . . . Crystal won't like that,' Felicity said almost to herself.

'Like that, is it? Oh, I guess she'll soon console herself with someone else. She's like that, or so I've been told. Look, I'm sorry about all this. Would you mind filling me in about the tour? I don't know why they bothered to do this. The best part of it's over anyway. That Mrs Harcourt must have been very insistent.'

Oh, yes, she must have been, thought Felicity, when at last she was alone. How had she managed to create so much enmity with Crystal that she had determinedly destroyed her career? Up to now she had had an outstanding reputation as a courier. She had never had anything else but praise about the way she had run the tours. And now this. She felt utterly shattered. She did not know how long she had been sitting there when there was a knock at the door and in walked Trent. Of course, he could still smile, she thought bitterly. It had all been a joke to him and now it was over.

'Well, so our tour is being cut short rather abruptly,' he commented. 'Pity about that, and rather shortsighted of your firm, I must say. What could have caused them to do this kind of thing, I wonder?'

He can't know about Crystal, she thought. Well, if he doesn't guess, I won't tell him.

'But don't be depressed about losing your job, Felicity. When I get back to my usual role, I'll see what can be done about it!'

'Oh, no, you won't, Trent. I don't want any

favours from you. If they don't think I'm good enough, that's it.'

'My dear girl, a word in the right ear is always useful. Don't worry now. You'll have your job again as soon as you get back to Vancouver.'

'I hardly think so. The whole thing has been a failure. I must go back to Montreal and get an office job like I had before.'

'Can you do secretarial work?' he asked.

'Certainly, but being a courier is more exciting.'

'I could offer you a fill-in job while you're sorting out your travel firm. How about it?'

'No, Trent, I'll manage alone. I'll arrange to return to Vancouver tomorrow. There's no longer any point in staying here.'

'There I can help you,' said Trent. 'I'll send for my jet to come to Calgary and hire a car to get us there. We can be in Vancouver by afternoon. Now come on, Felicity. This you can't refuse.'

She remembered that first day when she had met him when they had flown high among the stars. No, she could not refuse to go with him. It would be the end of a chapter. She could not think any farther ahead.

To most of the passengers she said that she had been called away, but to Edith and Anne, who had become friends, she told the truth. They were deeply shocked and could not understand the firm's action.

'We'll talk to them when we get back,' they promised.

'I doubt that will do any good,' said Felicity.

Trent acted with his usual drive and next afternoon they were on their way. Once more she was in the elegant executive jet, soaring above the earth. They were flying low most of the time and soon she could see the wheatfields of Alberta in golden squares, unfolding like a patchwork quilt below. How like, yet unlike this journey was from the first she had taken in this plane. Here was Trent sitting at her side, but oh, now how familiar was the sensation of sitting beside him, the warmth of his strong body so intimate and dear. But when at last they reached Vancouver, she would have to part from him, for there was no way she was going to let him plead for her with the travel firm.

Now he had left her and was up front talking to the pilot. As he came back, she noticed his smile, mysterious and yet somehow wicked. There was something satanic about his eyebrows, she thought, arched in amusement above the golden eyes.

'My staid Felicity, sitting there so calm and well-mannered, I'd better break it to you, I suppose. You've just been hijacked.'

She mistrusted the quality of his smile.

'What do you mean?' she asked.

'I'm kidnapping you. You thought you were going to Vancouver, but you're not. We're going to my ranch in Alberta. What do you think of that?'

'But you can't do that!' Felicity protested.

'I'm doing it. Listen to me. I knew there was no way you would come with me if I asked you to, but now you have no choice. There's no point in going back to Vancouver yet. You're out of a job and I don't have to end my vacation for a few days still. You need time to recuperate after all the fuss with your various passengers. You'll enjoy the ranch, I promise you. We can ride, swim, walk if you like and, I hope, there'll be no one to interrupt us whenever we want to make love.'

'But I have no intention of making love! I thought I'd made that fact quite clear on a number of occasions.'

'Not clear enough, my Felicity. Have you forgotten what happened or was about to happen at Lake Maligne? If you have, I most certainly haven't.'

'It won't happen again,' she assured him.

'Don't be so sure. Oh, Felicity, why will you persist in denying your own passionate nature? If only you would surrender to me, we could have a time of absolute beauty, I can promise you that.'

'I don't believe you.'

I'm lying, she thought. It could be beautiful. But what of the future? There could be nothing but bitter memories.

'I'll make you believe me. When we're alone at the ranch, you'll have to believe me, because it's going to happen, you can be sure of that.'

Felicity had a moment of sheer terror, when she looked into the golden flame of his eyes, and yet, at this very moment, her body longed for the rapture that only he could bring her. With a sensation of panic she thought, now he'll get his way. I'm too weak to go on resisting him. What's the use of refusing the very thing that I long to have? But what do I long for? Not only bodily passion to be over in a few days. I want love for a lifetime, and with Trent that's impossible. But would it not be better to accept that, to give in to temptation, to have this beautiful experience even if his feeling for me is only a temporary attraction, spurred on by my resistance to him, a desire for another conquest and one that hasn't been as easy as he's used to. When it's time for me to go, he'll forget me as easily as he's forgotten, say, Crystal.

The plane was descending now and soon it started to circle. Below them was a small airfield with hangar and windsock, and nearby was a spreading white mansion with a patio and blue swimming pool. Trent put his arm around her, turned her face upwards to him and, stroking her cheek with his hand, said, 'Don't look so worried, Felicity. I can promise you you're never going to regret this. It was fated to happen this way, a few days of heaven snatched from the ordinary world.'

But as he turned to look out of the window now that the plane was almost on the ground, something made him catch his breath as though he had been surprised.

'Oh, lord, it seems we have company. I might have known!'

Standing at a distance from the plane as it descended were two figures, and, as Felicity came down the steps that the pilot had let down, she saw the smaller figure detach himself from his place next to the other one and run shouting towards them.

'Hi, Pa!' he said, and jumped upon Trent with a tight embrace.

'Hi, Junior. What a surprise! I didn't expect to see you here.'

He was a boy of about eight years, and the thing that immediately struck Felicity was his distinct resemblance to Trent. He could have been Trent in miniature. It was quite laughable really, except that at this moment Felicity didn't feel like laughing.

'Mom didn't like it out East,' the boy was telling Trent. 'She was always crying, so she said we'd come here and we could ride and swim and lie in the sun. We hoped you'd be here, but we didn't know, and then you weren't. It'll be terrific now. Can I ride Sultan this time? Mom said I wouldn't be able to if you weren't here.'

'All in good time. Hi, Catherine.'

The boy's mother had come towards them more slowly.

'Hi, Trent. I hoped you'd come.'

She was a beautiful woman with curling dark hair and large grey eyes. She put up her face to be kissed and then was in his arms, clinging to him and crying a little.

'What is it?' he asked. 'More trouble?'

She gave a little nod and laughed shakily.

'We'll talk later,' she said, 'when we're alone.'

She glanced towards Felicity and Trent murmured an introduction which Felicity hardly heard. He seemed shaken, but no wonder. Who was Catherine? He had said he had no wife nor ever wanted one, but here was someone who must at least have had an intimate relationship with him for a great number of years. Could she be an ex-wife? But he had been so emphatic on the subject of alimony. His mistress? The boy was at least eight. She could be part of his past, but most certainly was part of the present too. There's one thing certain, Felicity thought. I'm leaving as soon as possible. What an embarrassing situation, and yet Trent seems to be taking it in his stride. Of course he would.

Catherine showed Felicity to a room that was furnished in Old Colonial style with a fourposter bed and pretty quilt, bright rugs and a highly polished floor.

'I think you'll be comfortable here,' she said, sounding embarrassed. 'I guess we've come here at a time we aren't wanted, but as soon as I've had a talk with Trent, we'll go again. Junior will be disappointed, because he sees so little of Trent and he adores him, but it can't be helped. I try not to interfere with Trent's private life now and he doesn't usually interfere in mine. But sometimes I have to turn to him for help. I have no one else and he's always been great to me, even though we haven't always seen eye to eye on various things. We row like crazy, but we usually come back together in the end.'

'Please don't go on my account,' said Felicity. 'I won't be staying.'

'No? Oh, don't leave, please. I hate Trent to be mad at me, and if you go, he'll think it's my fault.'

Poor woman, she has such a sad face, thought Felicity. This is how I could become if I were involved with Trent. She's an absolute slave to him. Imagine saying she'll go so that his latest attraction can stay! And yet I like her. There's something charming about her. But no, I must never be enslaved like her, tolerant of his other loves. I couldn't do it.

'You mustn't think of leaving,' she said. 'I can't tell you how glad I am you're here.'

And that was true, she thought. I was about to do something very foolish, but now, after meeting Catherine and her son, it's over. Between Trent and his kisses would always come the sad face of this other woman. Of this I'm sure.

Later that evening, Trent came to her.

'I'll have to have a session with Catherine this evening, I'm afraid. Too bad this had to happen on our first night here, but I hope they'll be gone by tomorrow. They never stay very long. Catherine is very restless. We haven't lived together for years, but she always arrives here at the first sign of trouble, whether about money or something more personal. I'm very fond of her, always have been. And Junior's a great guy, the kind of son any father would like to have. I wish I could have more time with him.'

But why don't you? thought Felicity. Oh, Trent, all your values are upside down. If I had a little son, the image of you . . . but I never shall.

Before the sun set, she saw them riding together, man and boy, very upright on their horses against the golden light in the West. As they rode back towards the stables she could hear them laughing together and she could see that Junior, in his cowboy hat and dude outfit, looked utterly thrilled with life. There's no place for me here, she thought.

Later, when the boy had been persuaded to go to

bed, tired out and happy, Trent excused himself to Felicity and he and Catherine went into the library. Felicity was left in the living room in front of the log fire that Trent had lit because the evening was chilly. She felt now utterly alone. This was much worse than when she had been on the tour. There at least she had had her passengers to occupy her mind, but here there was nothing she could do but face up to the fact that Trent was now lost to her and plan how she could get away. She had heard Catherine say that they had come by train and then hitched a lift to the ranch, and if Catherine could do that, so could she. She only had one suitcase and it was not very heavy. Yes, that was it. She would get up at first light and leave here. She would go to her room now, lock herself in, leave in the morning and never see Trent again. And that would be the end of the whole sorry episode.

But she was too late at least to carry out the first part of her plan. She had remained sitting too long looking into the fire, dreaming a little of Trent, seeing his loved features in the glowing heart of the flame, and now the door opened and she heard his step as he came towards her.

'Catherine asked to be excused. She's been a bit emotional, you understand. She says she hopes to see you in the morning before she goes.'

Ah, but she won't see me, thought Felicity. I'll be gone before she is, and if she finds I've gone, maybe she'll stay. She has the right to stay, surely. But I should say that. I should tell Trent the truth, that I intend to leave and that, as far as I'm concerned, something is over that never really began. But Trent was sitting beside her now and he had taken her in his arms. She felt his kisses like butterflies at first, then gaining strength, fierce and demanding, until she felt weak with despair at the thought that she would never again experience this enchantment.

'It's no use, Trent,' she said, struggling away from him. 'I must leave. You must go back to Catherine. It's quite plain that she needs you, and even if you don't love her now, your son adores you. Anyone can see that.'

'My son? Ah, but, Felicity, he's not my son.'

'But what do you mean? How can you say that? He looks exactly like you.'

'So I'm told, but I guess nephews sometimes look like their uncles. Something to do with genes, I suppose.'

'Nephew? But I thought . . . I thought . . .'

She saw the strong brown column of his throat quiver with laughter.

'Oh, my dear Felicity, what have you been thinking of me? Catherine is my sister, always very dear to me because she and I were brought up together in very poor conditions. We're very close because we were sent from one foster-home to another when we were young. Sometimes we were separated, but always we managed to come together again somehow. Then she married a no-good and since then her life has been less than happy, but foolishly she's still in love with him, and I help her out when I'm needed. She spends quite a lot of time at the house in Vancouver. I furnished the room that you had specially to please her. Don't you remember you used her gown? But how can you have imagined that Junior was my son?'

'He called you "Pa",' said Felicity, her mind in a whirl.

'Short for Pardner. He started calling me that when he was a little fellow who couldn't talk properly, and somehow it stuck. He's always been crazy about Westerns. But what did you think of Catherine? That she was my divorced wife or something?'

'That or your mistress, someone of long-standing intimacy anyway. I'm sorry, Trent, I realise now I was mistaken, but you didn't say she was your sister —at least I didn't grasp that.'

'I guess I didn't introduce you two properly. I was confused. I hate to see her unhappy, especially at a time when I was expecting so much happiness from you.'

'Don't say that, Trent, I can't bear it. I've got to tell you—I've decided to go tomorrow. I was going to slip away, hitch a lift to the railway, but now I can't deceive you. I've got to go.'

'Why, Felicity, why?'

He held her chin in his hands. looking into her eyes. She remembered how she had thought, when she had first seen him, that he was a man who would be difficult to lie to. Now she decided she would say it, just once and never again.

'I love you,' she said. 'That's why I'm leaving.'

His arms were around her now and he gave her a long gentle kiss.

'Could anything be more beautiful?' he said. 'Oh, my dear Felicity, I've waited so long for you to say those words.'

'But don't you understand?' she cried. 'I love you, but I can't stay with you. I can't bear to have the shortlived kind of affair that's all you want, like your affair with Crystal.'

'I had no affair with Crystal. Is that what you thought? Oh, yes, that morning on the boat, you taxed me with spending the night with her.'

'Forgive me—it had nothing to do with me. I shouldn't have said that.'

'You made me angry,' Trent explained. 'I wasn't going to deny it, when so obviously you wouldn't have believed me, but please believe me now. I spent the night most uncomfortably on a reclining chair, not at all in the circumstances you imagined. That's why I was up so early—and I was rewarded, may I remind you, with an exquisite kiss.'

Felicity looked into the clear golden eyes.

'I do believe you now,' she said. 'But I thought you and Crystal . . .'

'My innocent Felicity, don't you realise why Crystal has been so vindictive towards you? What's the saying . . . "Hell hath no fury". She made very amorous approaches to me, but finally I infuriated her by letting her know quite plainly that it was no go.'

'But the bracelet . . . you gave her the bracelet.'

'What bracelet?'

'The one you offered to me.'

He groped in his pocket.

'My sweet darling, here it is. I've been carrying it around with me all this time, hoping that some day you would accept it from me. You thought I gave it to Crystal? No, she must have bought one herself. I didn't even notice it.'

'Oh, Trent, I'm sorry, but how could I know? However, I still can't take it from you.'

'Not even if I tell you that I love you, that I've loved you all this time? Why do you think I came on this infuriating coach tour, if I didn't love you, tell me that?'

'Oh, no,' protested Felicity, 'how can you say that? No, Trent, we're opposites in our idea of love. I've told you from the first that I'm not the kind to enjoy a light and brief affair. So please don't say you love me, because it isn't what I mean by love, and I still say I must go.'

'Who's talking about a brief affair?' he asked.

'You are. All the time you said you didn't believe in long attachments.'

'So what kind of fool was I?' said Trent. 'Oh, my dear Felicity, for all this time I've been telling you I can teach you about love, but now I've found that it's you who must teach me. You can teach me about the kind of love that will last a lifetime. Do you think you're willing to do that, my sweet Felicity, even if it means marrying me?'

'Very willingly,' she said.

With his fingers he traced the shape of her mouth before bringing his lips to rest hard and sure upon her own.

'We'll persuade Catherine to stay for the wedding,' he said: 'Let it be soon. Clever Catherine—she said the moment she saw us together, she knew I'd met my fate.'